Clive Oxen
Christina La

with Jane Huds

ENGLISH FILE

upper-intermediate **workbook**

WITH KEY

OXFORD
UNIVERSITY PRESS

OXFORD
UNIVERSITY PRESS

Great Clarendon Street, Oxford OX2 6DP

Oxford University Press is a department of the University of Oxford. It furthers the University's objective of excellence in research, scholarship, and education by publishing worldwide in

Oxford New York

Athens Auckland Bangkok Bogotá Buenos Aires Cape Town Chennai Dar es Salaam Delhi Florence Hong Kong Istanbul Karachi Kolkata Kuala Lumpur Madrid Melbourne Mexico City Mumbai Nairobi Paris São Paulo Shanghai Singapore Taipei Tokyo Toronto Warsaw

with associated companies in Berlin Ibadan

Oxford and Oxford English are registered trade marks of Oxford University Press in the UK and in certain other countries

ISBN 0 19 436863 7

Printed in Spain by Unigraf Artes Gráficas, S. L.

The authors would like to thank Paul Seligson and Carmen Dolz for the *English sounds* chart.

The Publisher and Authors are grateful to those who have given permission to reproduce the following extracts and adaptations of copyright material:

p.6 'Family Gatherings' from *The Xenophobes Guide to The English* by Antony Miall & David Milstead. Published by Oval Books 1993, 1999. Reproduced by permission of Oval Books; p.9 'Woodward condemns the 'soap opera' of trial by television' by Alison Boshoff. Appeared in *The Telegraph* September 1 1998 p.4. Reproduced by permission of Telegraph Group Ltd; p.12 'Revealed, the science of splitting your sides with laughter' by David Derbyshire. Appeared in *Daily Mail* 29 January 1999. Reproduced by permission of Daily Mail/Atlantic Syndication Partners; p.16 'Why men won't go to the Doctor' by Anita Chaudhuri. Appeared in *The Times* 4 May 2000. Reproduced by permission of Times Newspapers Ltd; p.22 'Some need it hot, says curry addiction study' by Mark Henderson. Appeared in *The Times* 25 October 2000. Reproduced by permission of Times Newspapers Ltd; p.26 'Maid to serve' by Emily Tilton and 'Final Witness' by Candice C. Mutschler from *The World's Shortest Stories*, edited by Steve Moss. Copyright © 1998, 1995 Steve Moss, published by Running Press Book Publishers, Philadelphia and London. Reproduced by permission; p.29 Extracts from *Ghosts of Everest: The Search for Mallory and Irvine*. Copyright © 1999 Jochen Hemmleb, Larry Johnson and Eric Simonson. Originally published by The Mountaineers,

Seattle, WA, USA. British Edition Published by Macmillan Publishers Ltd. Reproduced by permission of The Mountaineers Books; p.32 'Elizabeth I: A Queen with the Heart and Stomach of a King' From *Horrible Histories: Terrible Tudors* by Terry Deary. Published by Scholastic Ltd 1993. Reproduced by permission of Scholastic Ltd; p.36 'Why did I wear that?' Appeared in *The Sunday Times Style Magazine* Feb/March 2000. Reproduced by permission of Times Newspapers Ltd; p.39 'Bad Sports' by Laura Marcus. Appeared in *Options Magazine* August 1994. © Laura Marcus/Options/IPC Syndication. Reproduced by permission of IPC Syndication; p.42 'Motorists told to drive out road rage with Feng Shui' by Harry Cooke. Appeared in *The Express* 3 December 1998. Reproduced by permission of Express Newspapers; p.46 'Still king of the swingers' by Lucy Broadbent. Appeared in *The Mail on Sunday* 16 March 1997. Reproduced by permission of Mail on Sunday/Atlantic Syndication; p.49 Extracts from *Mind Matters* by Alan Maley and Francoise Grellet, 1981 Cambridge University Press. Reproduced by permission of Cambridge University Press; p.52 'Premonitions – a vision of the future?' from *Premonitions and How to Deal with Them* by Alan Vaughan. Appeared in Fate, 49, 1 (1966). Reproduced by permission of Alan Vaughan; p.56 'Blundering pickpocket's run-in with fastest man on Earth' by Giles Tremlett. Appeared in *The Times* 19 August 1999. Reproduced by permission of Times Newspapers Ltd; p.59 'Pinkerton papers lift the lid on Wild West Justice' by Ben Mcintyre. Appeared in *The Times* 2 June 2000. Reproduced by permission of Times Newspapers Ltd; p.62 'If little girls could vote, Barbie would be President.' by Hannah Betts. Appeared in *The Times* 3 May 2000. Reproduced by permission of Times Newspapers Ltd; p.66 'The Nova Awards in Communication' by David Maule. Appeared in *Modern English Teacher* Volume 9, No 2 2000. Reproduced by permission of Modern English Teacher / Pearson Education; p.69 Extracts from *Notes From a Big Country* by Bill Bryson. Copyright © Bill Bryson 1998. Published in paperback by Blackswan, a division of Transworld Publishers. All rights reserved. Reproduced by permission of Transworld Publishers; p.72 Extracts from *The Genius of Shakespeare* by Professor Jonathan Bate. Published by Picador. Reproduced by permission of Macmillan Publishers Ltd & David Godwin Associates.

Although every effort has been made to trace and contact copyright holders before publication, this has not been possible in some cases. We apologize for any apparent infringement of copyright and if notified, the publisher will be pleased to rectify any errors or omissions at the earliest opportunity.

Designed by Amanda Hockin

Illustrations by:

Wendy Blundell pp.36, 43; Cartoonstock pp.4 (Baines) 11 (Roystock), 38 (Neil Bennett); Mark Draisey pp.27, 66; Mark Duffin pp.8, 31, 48, 61; Martin Fish pp.12, 28, 39, 49, 60,70; Neil Gower p.45; David Hopkins p.18; Ed McLachlan pp.6, 15, 21, 24 30, 40, 42, 47, 50, 51, 54, 58; Katherine Walker pp.7, 10, 20, 25, 35, 36, 41, 37, 53; Annabel Wright pp.26, 43, 52, 67.

Commissioned photography by David Tolley p.63.

The Publishers would like to thank the following for their kind permission to reproduce photographs:

Associated Press pp.46 (MGM), 53; Camera Press p.19 (Roland Boyes/Sir David Steele, S. Soames/Margaret Foster); Robert Harding Picture Library p.28; Mervyn Hudson p.32; Kobal Collection p.59 (20th Century Fox); Press Association pp.19 (Michael Crabtree), 56 (EPA), 64 (Beatles); Rex Features pp.9 (Kevin Wisniewski), 18 (JSU), 22 (James Fraser), 32 (JHS/Polygram), 62, 64 (Sipa/Villard/Naomi Campbell), 72 (Miramax Films/Universal Pictures); Royal Geographical Society p.33 (George Mallory, Andrew Irving); Frank Spooner p.69 (Gamma); Stone pp.13 (Charles Gupton), 16 (Alan Thornton), 29 (Chris Noble); Manuel Tenas p.33; John Walmsley p.23.

Contents

What's in a name?

> 'Forgive your enemies, but never forget their names.'
>
> *J F Kennedy, US president*

GRAMMAR

1 CHECK WHAT YOU KNOW: Phrasal verbs

Replace the *expressions* with a phrasal verb in the correct form to make the sentences more informal. Use a verb and a preposition from each box.

be	go		away	down
give	pick		out	on
hold	throw		up (x3)	over
turn	wake			

PHRASAL VERB

EXAMPLE
They *ended their relationship*.   *broke up*

1 Peter *stops sleeping* at 6 o'clock every morning.   _____

2 Oliver decided to *stop* smoking after visiting the doctor.   _____

3 When the match *finished*, the spectators went home.   _____

4 He *put* the old newspapers *in the rubbish bin*.   _____

5 When I phoned, the secretary asked me to *wait for a moment*.   _____

6 They told us we could *collect* the tickets at the theatre.   _____

7 *Make* the television *quieter*, please! It's too loud.   _____

8 Susie *left the house* and shut the door.   _____

2 NEW LANGUAGE: Verbs with two prepositions

Complete the phrasal verbs with a word from box 1 and a word from box 2.

1	down	forward	on	out

2	of	on	to	with

1 We're running _____ _____ petrol. We'll have to stop at the next garage.

2 Children always look _____ _____ Christmas because of the presents!

3 My uncle looks _____ _____ my father because he's unemployed.

4 My son gets _____ well _____ his cousins because they're the same age.

3 Separable or non-separable?

Rewrite the sentence, substituting the **noun** with a pronoun. Change the word order if necessary.

EXAMPLE Look up **the new words**!
    Look them up!

1 I look like **my mother**.
   I _____ .

2 You must cross out **the wrong words**.
   You must _____ .

3 Switch off **the TV** when the film finishes.
   _____ .

4 My mother looks after **my baby daughter** when I'm at work.
   _____ .

5 Send back **the sweater** if you don't like it.
   _____ .

6 Look through **the contract** before you sign it.
   _____ .

7 Turn up **the radio**. I can't hear it.
   _____ .

8 My son takes after **his father**.
   _____ .

He certainly takes after his dad!

4 Guessing the meaning

a Look at some different meanings of these particles.

up	down	on
1 increase	1 decrease	1 continue
2 completely	2 put on paper	2 wear
	3 stop completely	3 connect
off	**out**	
1 disconnect	1 make disappear	
2 depart	2 to different people	

b Focus on the meaning of the particles in phrasal verbs a–g. Write the correct number in the box.

a If you keep **on** shouting, I'll get angry. ☐ *1*

b The government has promised to bring **down** the cost of transport. ☐

c He got onto the motorbike and drove **off**. ☐

d It's your birthday so you have to blow **out** the candles. ☐

e They've put **up** the price of cigarettes by 30%. ☐

f The factory closed **down** two years ago, and the workers had to find new jobs. ☐

g Make sure you don't leave the lights **on** when you go out. ☐

VOCABULARY

5 Remember words from the text

Complete the texts.

1 Some people think that the name you are given doesn't matter. It's completely ¹**irr**_____ to how well you do in life. I'm not ²**aw**_____ of having had any problems with my name, though I know it's not very popular at the moment. In any case most people ³**te**_____ to choose names which are in fashion.

2 We're still a bit undecided about where to go for our summer holiday, but we really need to ¹**m**_____ up our ²**m**_____ soon, as it's already April. One thing we'll have to take into ³**a**_____ is that we've got a young child, so we don't want to go anywhere too hot.

6 Word-building: Nouns from verbs

Make nouns from the verbs. Use your dictionary to help you.

1 decide _____   5 succeed _____

2 tend _____   6 affect _____

3 associate _____ 7 advise _____

4 choose _____   8 compare _____

7 Phrasal verbs

a Complete with the correct particle.

When my son was born everybody immediately said he **looked** exactly ¹_____ his father, and as he was the only son he was **named** ²_____ him too. But in personality I think he **takes** ³_____ me. In fact, although we have always **got** ⁴_____ really well, we sometimes argue just because we're so similar. Even though we lived in France, I **brought** him ⁵_____ in a very British way – big breakfasts, and bed at 7.30. Now that he has **grown** ⁶_____ – he's twenty-one – I don't see him as often as I'd like.

b Complete with a phrasal verb with *get*.

1 What time do you usually _____ _____ in the morning?

2 Hurry up and _____ _____ the car. We're leaving in a minute.

3 Do you _____ _____ well with your in-laws?

4 You have to _____ _____ the bus at the next stop.

5 You need to work hard at school if you want to _____ _____ in life.

8 Pronunciation: Word stress

Underline the stressed syllable in these words.

1 stereotype   9 association

2 applicant   10 effect

3 tendency   11 aware

4 research   12 account

5 old-fashioned   13 contradict

6 glamorous   14 unpopular

7 irrelevant   15 dramatic

8 attitude

READING AND WRITING

9 Reading

a Read the text once and find out when English families usually meet. Ignore the gaps.

FAMILY GATHERINGS

1 ☐, the English would not dream of spending their Christmas anywhere else but with the family. This annual festival almost always ends in tears and to get over it takes many families at least months. But tradition rules and, when October comes, English families are beginning to plan for another family Christmas, having apparently completely forgotten the chaos of the one before.

2 ☐, family members avoid each other throughout the year except on compulsory occasions such as baptisms, weddings and funerals. Of these, baptisms and funerals, being the shortest, are the most popular. Weddings usually end up as major battles – the only difference being the uniforms of the people taking part.

3 ☐, and so do the arguments. Even though English etiquette books try to help by pointing out who is responsible for organising and paying for the bride's dress, the flowers, the church, the choir, the organist, the cars, the reception, the food, the photographers and the ambulance service, the English will fight furiously on every single issue for months before, during and even after the great day.

4 ☐ that these meetings ever take place at all.

b Match the first words of each paragraph to the correct paragraph. Write the letter in the box.

A It is still the triumph of English hope over English experience

B Planning for weddings starts early

C Although they are the least family-orientated people on earth

D Apart from Christmas

c Match the highlighted words to the definitions.

1 a woman on or just before her wedding day _____

2 recover from sth _____

3 happen _____

4 a group of people who sing together _____

5 drops of water that come out of your eyes, e.g. when you cry _____

6 a problem or subject for discussion _____

7 the ceremony when sb becomes a member of a Christian church, and is given a name _____

8 the rules of polite and correct behaviour _____

10 Writing: Using paragraphs

a Divide the following composition into four paragraphs. Draw three lines to show where you think the new paragraphs should start.

. . . .

Should parents name their children after themselves?

In one family I know, every time the mother calls out the name David, two people simultaneously shout 'Yes?'. This is one example of how confusing it must be to live in a house where two people have the same name, but there are more disadvantages. /The first and most important disadvantage is the everyday confusion in the house. Secondly other people, for example, postmen and bank managers can also get confused. Thirdly, and more importantly, children in this situation may find it difficult to form their own sense of identity. On the other hand, there is one advantage of giving your child the same name as yourself and that is that you are continuing a family tradition. The idea of the family is very important in our society and this is one way of making sure that a child feels part of it. In conclusion, I think every parent should give their child whatever name they like, but they should remember that the wide range of names available helps to add variety to our lives. New names mean progress and modernity. Names that have been in the family suggest that we are more traditional.

. . . .

The winner takes it all

'The press is ferocious. It forgives nothing, it only hunts for mistakes.'
Diana, Princess of Wales

GRAMMAR

1 NEW LANGUAGE: Indirect questions

Reorder the words to make sentences.

1 called know is ~~do~~ latest you album what their

Do _____ ?

2 remember *American Pie* lyrics you wrote the ~~can~~ who for

Can _____ ?

3 me you goes this ~~could~~ bus if tell Chelsea to

Could _____ ?

4 is house ~~do~~ where remember you their

Do _____ ?

5 box tell closes ~~can~~ when me the you office

Can _____ ?

6 or know not coming whether you ~~do~~ he's

Do _____ ?

2 Questions ending in prepositions

a Complete the dialogue with a suitable short question. (question word + a preposition, e.g. *Who from?*)

PAUL	I was talking to Steve last night.
TOM	Oh? [1]_____ ?
PAUL	That Lou Reed concert we're going to next week.
TOM	What's the problem?
PAUL	Steve can't come because he's going away.
TOM	Oh no. [2]_____ ?
PAUL	To London.
TOM	[3]_____ ?
PAUL	He's going for ten days.
TOM	[4]_____ ?
PAUL	He's got a job interview, I think, and he wants to prepare for it.
TOM	[5]_____ ?
PAUL	With some chemical company.
TOM	So why don't you sell his ticket then?
PAUL	[6]_____ ? Everyone I know's already got one.

b Now write full questions for each short question.

1 *What were you talking about?*

2 _____

3 _____

4 _____

5 _____

6 _____

3 Questions with or without *do/did*

Right ✓ or wrong ✗ ? Correct the wrong questions.

1 Who did write this awful article? ☐

2 How many people you think like violent films? ☐

3 Who did they interview on the chat show last night? ☐

4 Which newspaper does use the most dramatic headlines? ☐

5 What said the papers about the film? ☐

6 How many viewers watched the cup final last weekend? ☐

7 Which channels don't have commercials in your country? ☐

8 Which presenter you like best? ☐

VOCABULARY

4 Revision: The cinema

a Complete the text with words from the list. What's the name of the film?

base   cast   directed   parts   played   set   plot   starred

. . . .

This film was ¹_____ in Washington in 1974, and was ²_____ by Alan Pakula in 1976. The ³_____ is ⁴_____ on the true story of the Watergate scandal. It ⁵_____ Robert Redford and Dustin Hoffman who ⁶_____ the ⁷_____ of two journalists from the *Washington Post* who eventually uncover the lies that bring down President Nixon. The ⁸_____ also included Jason Robards who won the Oscar for Best Supporting Actor.

. . . .

b Write words for the definitions.

1 the music of a film   _ _ u _ _ t _ _ _ _ _

2 images in a film often created by computer   _ p _ _ _ _ _ _
   e _ _ _ _ _ _

3 part of a film happening in one place   _ c _ _ _ _

4 translated into another language   d _ _ _ _ _ d

5 verb meaning *to film*   _ _ o o _

5 The media

Complete the puzzle to find the mystery word.

1 the number of people watching a TV programme (8,7)

2 a TV programme giving factual information about a particular subject

3 the titles of newspaper articles printed in large letters above the story

4 to be unfairly influenced, e.g. by a political party

5 a newspaper with small pages, a lot of pictures and short simple articles

6 a person whose job is to collect, write or publish news

7 to send out radio or television programmes

8 a TV programme where famous people are interviewed (4,4)

9 a person who watches television

10 a story about the lives and problems of a group of people which continues every day or several times a week (4,5)

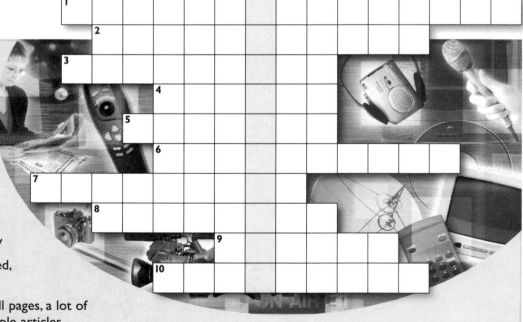

6 Prepositions: *in* or *on*?

Complete with *in* or *on*.

1 _____ the front page
2 _____ the news
3 _____ TV
4 _____ the radio
5 _____ the phone
6 _____ the papers

7 Pronunciation: Recognizing phonetics

Write the media words. Practise saying them.

1 /ˈkɒmədi/   _____
2 /fəˈtɒɡrəfə/   _____
3 /kɑːˈtuːnz/   _____
4 /feɪk/   _____
5 /ˈsensəʃɪp/   _____
6 /ˈɔːdiəns/   _____

READING AND WRITING

8 Reading

a Read the text and find out if Louise is for or against the use of cameras in the courtroom and why.

Woodward condemns the 'soap opera' of trial by television

LOUISE WOODWARD was the 18-year old nanny convicted in 1998 by a court in the United States of murdering the infant Matthew Eappen. Recently she spoke about her experience of a televised court case at the Edinburgh Television Festival.

Louise criticised the televising of trials. 'It should never be the case of looking into a defendant's eyes and making a decision on their guilt or innocence,' she told the Edinburgh Television Festival. 'It should be the law that decides on a person's guilt, but television, with its human and emotional interest, takes the attention away from this.'

Although she thought it was an inevitable development, she added: 'Television turns everything into entertainment. We should remember that in the end courtrooms are serious places. It is people's lives and future lives that you are dealing with. It is not a soap opera and people should not see it like that. Serious issues should not be trivialised.'

She admitted that she had found it difficult to live a normal life since returning to Britain. She blamed the publicity on the televising of her trial, which was shown on Sky News in this country. 'I get asked for interviews every day by television, radio, and newspapers about my future and I turn them down. I never wanted to be in the public eye. I just hope the press will forget me as time passes.'

'I was never asked if I wanted cameras in the courtroom. It put a lot more pressure on me than I already had. If I had known that people were counting how often I blinked my eyes or scratched my nose, it would have been even more stressful.'

Glossary

trial	the process to decide if sb is innocent or guilty
defendant	a person accused of a crime
courtrooms	places where people accused of crimes are judged
blame	think that a person or thing is responsible for sth bad
turn down	refuse, reject
blink	open and shut your eye
scratch	rub your skin with your nails

b Read the text again with the glossary. Mark the sentences **T** (true) or **F** (false).

1 Louise thinks you can tell from someone's face if they are innocent or guilty. ☐

2 She thinks that TV trials are sure to become more common. ☐

3 She thinks that televising trials make them seem less important and serious than they really are. ☐

4 She has become well-known as a result of the televising of her trial. ☐

5 She has given a lot of interviews to the press since she returned to Britain. ☐

6 She had always hoped to be famous. ☐

7 She gave permission for her trial to be televised. ☐

8 The TV cameras made the trial more difficult for her. ☐

9 Writing: Questions

Complete the dialogue with suitable questions.

A 1 _____ TV tonight?

B Let's have a look. There's a film on after the weather forecast.

A 2 _____ on?

B BBC 1.

A 3 _____ called?

B *The English Patient.*

A 4 _____ about?

B It's about a Hungarian count who worked on a geographical expedition.

A 5 _____ set?

B In the Sahara Desert. It looks really good. The only problem is, it's a bit long.

A 6 _____ last?

B About three hours.

A 7 _____ in it?

B Some really good actors. Ralph Fiennes, Juliette Binoche and Kristin Scott-Thomas. I think we should watch it.

A 8 _____ start?

B In about five minutes.

Funny ha-ha?

GRAMMAR

1 CHECK WHAT YOU KNOW: Adverbs

a Revise the rules. Then do exercises **b** and **c**.

Use	Example	Notes/Problems
Use adverbs or adverbial expressions to describe a verb, an adjective/adverb, or a whole sentence.	*She sings beautifully.* *I'm incredibly tired.* *Luckily, we caught the train.*	To form an adverb from an adjective add *-ly* (see chart SB *p.19*). There are a few exceptions (*well, hard, fast*). ❶ Not all words ending in *-ly* are adverbs, e.g. *friendly* is an adjective.

b Right ☑ or wrong ☒? Correct the wrong adverbs.

1 carefuly ☐ _____
2 badly ☐ _____
3 goodly ☐ _____
4 fastly ☐ _____
5 nearly ☐ _____
6 dayly ☐ _____
7 correctly ☐ _____
8 wonderfully ☐ _____
9 extremly ☐ _____
10 actualy ☐ _____

c Cross out the incorrect word in each sentence.

1 We all waited *nervous/nervously* outside the exam room.

2 My father has never had an accident because he drives really *good/well*.

3 We thought very *careful/carefully* about it.

4 Richard speaks Italian *perfect/perfectly*.

5 The interviewer's voice was so *quiet/quietly* that I could hardly hear her.

6 My children behaved really *bad/badly* at my best friend's wedding.

2 NEW LANGUAGE: Adverbs: word order

Mark with a * the possible position(s) for each adverb or adverbial phrase.

1 *Jenny went to the hairdresser's*. (last week)

2 I'm sorry about the accident. (very)

3 You should swim in cold water after a heavy meal. (never)

4 She speaks French and she's good at German. (also)

5 We want to set off early. (ideally)

6 Prices go up during the summer. (usually)

7 I'm sure I left my keys at home. (quite)

8 The paparazzi followed them into the hotel. (even)

3 Adverbs: Meaning

Cross out the adverb which has a **different** meaning.

EXAMPLE
Joy hasn't watched the news *recently/~~late~~/lately*.

1 The firemen *near/nearly/almost* died while they were putting out the fire.

2 Our car broke down but *eventually/in the end/at the end* we arrived.

3 His latest film is *far/much/fairly* better than the one before.

4 That house is *incredibly/extremely/slightly* expensive – only a millionaire could buy it!

5 I'm feeling *a little/slightly/very* nervous about my driving test.

6 I thought he was about 50 but *in fact/actually/nowadays* he's 65.

7 It's *completely/quite/rather* true. I promise!

8 *At the moment/Right now/Actually* I've got a lot of work to do.

VOCABULARY

4 Words related to humour

Complete the text with words from the list.

comedian fun funny joke laugh make fun of
pulling their leg sense of humour witty

"You see a lot more with these widescreen TVs."

It is a well-known fact that people with a good
¹_____ not only enjoy life more, but can actually live longer, too. It is not necessary to be a professional ²_____ to make people ³_____ ; most people can usually tell at least one good ⁴_____ which will be ⁵_____ enough for everybody to

laugh. People who are ⁶_____ (good at saying clever and amusing things) are also much appreciated by their friends, so long as they don't ⁷_____ them too much and maybe hurt their feelings. You can also often have a lot of ⁸_____ with your friends by ⁹_____ (telling them something which isn't true).

5 Adverbs

Complete with an adverb that means the same as the phrase in brackets. The first letter is given.

1 I _deally_ all medical treatment should be free. (in a perfect world)

2 G_____ the image became clearer. (little by little)

3 These scissors were s_____ designed for left-handed people. (for a particular reason)

4 O_____ this book wasn't written for children. (as can easily be seen)

5 A_____ , if you don't like it you can change it. (in any case)

6 A_____ it's a lovely place for a holiday. (according to what people say)

7 B_____ , this course is about communication skills. (looking at what's most important)

8 He seemed very unfriendly but a_____ he's just shy. (the fact is)

6 Use your dictionary: Confused words

a The following words from this unit often cause confusion. Read the definitions.

stranger /ˈstreɪndʒə/ n. a person that you do not know

foreigner /ˈfɒrənə/ n. a person from a country that is not your own

career /kəˈrɪə/ n. a job or series of jobs in a particular area of work, e.g. _She'd like a career in journalism._

course /kɔːs/ n. a complete series of lessons or studies

funny /ˈfʌni/ adj. something that makes you smile or laugh

enjoyable /ɪnˈdʒɔɪəbəl/ adj. something that gives pleasure

humour /ˈhjuːmə/ n. the funny or amusing qualities of sb/sth

mood /muːd/ n. the way that you feel at a particular time

b Complete the sentences with the correct word from each pair.

1 Don't talk to the boss today. She's not in a very good _____ .

2 We had a great time in Greece on holiday. It was really _____ .

3 When Jeremy has finished his _____ , he's going to look for a job as a professional musician.

4 _____ s can't understand why the British drive on the left.

5 We always tell children not to talk to _____ s .

6 A footballer's _____ is very short.

7 He's a very _____ person. He's got a great sense of _____ .

READING AND WRITING

7 Reading

a Read the article quickly. Why does Dr Ramachandran think we laugh?

b Read the text again and decide which answer is best, a, b, or c.

1 Scientists were interested in the Indian woman's case because
  a she had a serious head injury.
  b she had an unusual way of reacting to pain.
  c she couldn't stop laughing.

2 According to Dr Ramachandran, she laughed because
  a the pin didn't hurt.
  b part of her brain had been affected by her injury.
  c she thought the doctor was being funny.

3 Dr Ramachandran thinks that laughter is
  a one of the great mysteries of human nature.
  b an expression of surprise.
  c strongly connected to feelings of relief.

4 He says that prehistoric hunters laughed when
  a they stopped feeling afraid.
  b they saw a rabbit.
  c they were in danger.

c Underline any words you didn't know and try to guess their meaning from the context. Then check with your dictionary.

Revealed, the science of laughter

A funny thing happened when a middle-aged woman was taken into hospital – it helped a group of scientists to discover why people laugh. It appears that different types of laughing are 'all is well' signals which tell others when a threatening or confusing situation is safe.

The woman arrived at an Indian hospital with a head injury which appeared to give her a strange reaction to pain. Every time a doctor stuck a pin in her hand, she laughed uncontrollably.

According to Dr Vilayanur Ramachandran, neuroscientist at the University of California in San Diego, the region of her brain involved in sending messages about pain had been disconnected. He explained: 'Part of her brain was saying, "Look, there's pain" but the next part was saying, "There's no problem". As a result the brain sent out the "all is well" signal and she started laughing. There's no other theory that makes sense.'

Why we laugh is one of the great mysteries of human behaviour. But Dr Ramachandran believes he has found the answer. 'Laughter isn't just an expression of surprise; it is also strongly connected to feelings of relief,' he told the American Association for the Advancement of Science conference in Los Angeles yesterday.

He argued that laughter was a form of communication which helped our ancestors save energy and resources. If, for instance, prehistoric hunters were surprised by a sound in the bushes, their immediate instinct would be fear. Adrenalin levels would go up fast and they would prepare to fight or run away. But if the sound turned out to be a rabbit and not a danger, the natural reaction would be to laugh – sending out a signal to the whole group that they could relax.

8 Writing

Make the story more vivid by filling the gaps with a suitable adverb from the list. Use each adverb once.

at that moment   early   extremely   eventually   fast   immediately   just
luckily   yesterday   unfortunately

My friend Simon had an ¹_____ embarrassing experience ²_____ . He decided to go to the swimming pool in his lunchbreak, so he finished work ³_____ and got into his car. He couldn't drive ⁴_____ as there was a lot of traffic. When he ⁵_____ arrived at the pool, he got changed and ⁶_____ dived into the pool. ⁷_____ , the elastic broke on his swimming shorts as soon as he entered the water, and he watched them float away to the other end of the pool.

⁸_____ there was no-one else in the pool ⁹_____ , but ¹⁰_____ when Simon was swimming to get them, a girl came into the pool and picked them up, so Simon had to ask her to give him his shorts back!

LISTENING

1 Mad about classical music!

a **T1.1** Listen to an interview with Caroline, a 17-year-old violinist. Has she always wanted to play the violin?

b Listen again and choose the best answer, a, b, or c.

1 What was the main reason Caroline started playing the violin?

    a   Her parents were professional musicians.
    b   She liked listening to violin music.
    c   Her older sister was already learning to play an instrument.

2 The problem with her private lessons was that

    a   she preferred her mother as a teacher.
    b   it took a long time to get to the teacher's house.
    c   the lessons were boring.

3 Caroline wanted to give up the violin because

    a   she didn't have enough free time.
    b   she didn't have enough time for school work.
    c   she hated practising two hours a day.

4 She went back to playing the violin because

    a   her parents were very unhappy that she'd stopped.
    b   she realized that she had made a mistake.
    c   she was asked to play in a professional orchestra.

PRONUNCIATION

1 Vowel sounds

T1.3 Go to **Vocabulary Builder 1** *p. 126* in the Student's Book. Listen and repeat the words from the English sounds chart, and these words with the same sounds from File 1.

1 /ɪ/ critic, lyrics
2 /iː/ media, **CD**
3 /æ/ advertize, actually
4 /ɑː/ drama, laugh
5 /ɒ/ comedy, flop
6 /ɔː/ story, **au**dience
7 /ʊ/ look, pull
8 /uː/ news, humour
9 /ə/ photographer, editor
10 /ɜː/ journalist, verse
11 /e/ press, headlines
12 /ʌ/ fun, luckily
13 /eɪ/ fake, page
14 /əʊ/ soap, joke
15 /aɪ/ private life, biased
16 /aʊ/ account, **out**
17 /ɔɪ/ tabloid, noisy
18 /ɪə/ serious, nearly
19 /eə/ fairly, aware
20 /ʊə/ sure, endure

2 Intonation

T1.4 Copy the polite intonation in indirect questions.

3 Word stress

a Underline the stress in these words.

1 pseudonym
2 overcome
3 tendency
4 performance
5 chorus
6 stereotype
7 sensational
8 fortunately
9 automatically
10 especially

b **T1.5** Listen and repeat the words.

2 Living abroad

a **T1.2** Listen to British people talking about living abroad. Tick the speakers who think they will return to Britain.

b Listen again and complete the chart.

Name	✓	Where do they live?	What do they do?	How long have they lived there?	What is different from Britain?
Mike					
Cathy					
Susan					
Luke					

I told you I was ill

GRAMMAR

1 CHECK WHAT YOU KNOW: First and second conditionals

a Revise the rules. Then do exercise **b**.

Use	Example	Notes/Problems
Use **first conditional** (*if* + a present tense, *will/won't* or *going to* + infinitive, or an imperative) to talk about a **future possibility** and its consequence.	*If I see her, I'll tell her.* *If you've finished, let's go.* *He won't come if he isn't feeling better.* *If the film is very violent, I'm going to leave.*	After *if* you can use the present simple, present perfect, or present continuous but not a future form. NOT ~~if I'll see her ...~~ ❶ *unless* + positive verb can be used instead of *if ... not*, e.g. *He won't come unless he's feeling better.*
Use **second conditional** (*if* + past simple, *would/wouldn't* + infinitive) to talk about an **imaginary present or future situation** and its consequence.	*If we had more time, we'd meet more often.* *If I were taller, I'd be a policeman.* *She wouldn't come if she wasn't feeling well.* *If I won the lottery, I might stop working.*	(= but we haven't, so we can't.) You can use *was* or *were* in the *if* clause, e.g. *If I was taller ...* You can use the past continuous in the *if* clause. You can use *could* or *might* instead of *would* to talk about a possible consequence.

b Put the verb in brackets in the correct form.

1 If my GP can't cure my headaches, I _____ (try) acupuncture.

2 If your leg was broken, it _____ (hurt) more.

3 I'm sure you would feel better if you _____ (not smoke) so much.

4 If you _____ (not stop) eating so much salt, you'll get high blood pressure.

5 This ward would be less depressing if there _____ (be) fewer beds.

6 If your ankle _____ (not be) swollen, it's probably not serious.

7 The ambulance _____ (be) here in a minute, if there's no traffic.

8 If my grandfather _____ (not be) so fit, he wouldn't be able to live on his own.

9 She _____ (not go) to work unless she feels better.

2 NEW LANGUAGE: Future time clauses

a Right ☑ or wrong ☒ ? Correct the wrong sentences.

1 If the weather forecast is wrong again tomorrow, I don't watch it any more.

2 He's going to see the specialist as soon as he'll get the result of his tests.

3 I always get stressed if people shout at me.

4 They make up their minds as soon as they've looked round the house tomorrow.

5 Come and see me when you are feeling better.

6 If your headache will get worse you should go to bed.

7 I'm going to write down your number in case I'll need it.

8 He never goes to the doctor unless he's feeling really terrible.

b Cross out the wrong word.

1 He won't give the patient a prescription *when/until* he's examined him.

2 She'll be able to go home *as soon as/unless* she's completely got over the operation.

3 They'll start the treatment *in case/when* the diagnosis is confirmed.

4 You'd better take a sweater *if/in case* it's cold when you get there.

5 *If/Unless* that paper keeps on making up stories, I'll stop buying it.

6 I never take antibiotics *unless/in case* I've got an infection.

VOCABULARY

3 Health and medicine

a Write the words for the definitions.

1 the piece of paper on which a doctor writes the name of the medicine you need _____

2 saying exactly what illness a person has (*noun*) _____

3 a photo taken of the inside of the human body using a special light _____

4 a sudden illness which attacks the brain and can leave a person unable to move part of their body _____

5 a building where GPs see their patients _____ _____

6 an amount of a drug which is too much and therefore is not safe _____

7 (of a woman) having a baby developing in her body (*adjective*) _____

8 a change in your body which is a sign of illness _____

b Complete the text with a word or expression from the list.

acupuncture	cough	days off	GP	lose weight
make an appointment	put on	side effects	sneezing	virus

My father didn't feel well. He was ¹_____ a lot and had a bad ²_____ so he decided to ³_____ to see his ⁴_____ .The doctor told him he probably had a ⁵_____ and advised him to take a few ⁶_____ and rest. He also said he should stop smoking. My father said he had tried but couldn't, so the doctor recommended ⁷_____ . It was successful and he has now given up, but unfortunately there have been ⁸_____ : he has ⁹_____ nearly three kilos in two weeks. Soon he'll have to back to the doctor to ask how to ¹⁰_____ .

4 Use your dictionary: Body idioms

When you want to look up an idiom in the dictionary, e.g. *pull sb's leg*, you normally find it under the 'key' word, in this case **leg**.

Use your dictionary to find the missing verbs in these idioms. What do the idioms mean?

1 You've really _____ **your foot** in it this time. You should never have mentioned his ex-wife at dinner.

2 We don't _____ **eye to eye** at all about politics. She's right wing and I'm left wing.

3 I need help. Can someone _____ **me a hand**?

4 Could you _____ **an eye on** the milk? It's about to boil.

5 I've told her three times but it _____ **in one ear and out the other.**

6 Good luck for tomorrow! I'll _____ **my fingers crossed.**

5 Pronunciation

Look at the phonetics and write the words. Practise saying them. What do they mean?

1 /eɪk/ _____

2 /kjʊə/ _____

3 /ˈhæŋɡəʊvə/ _____

4 /ˈkrɒnɪk/ _____

5 /ˈsɜːdʒən/ _____

6 /ˈswəʊlən/ _____

7 /ˈdɪzi/ _____

8 /wɔːd/ _____

READING AND WRITING

6 Reading

a Read the article and underline three reasons why men don't go to the doctor as often as women.

Why men won't go to the doctor

1 ☐ At last there is scientific proof to back up what women have suspected for years – that when it comes to their health, men are big babies. Statistics revealed at the recent Royal Society of Medicine conference on men's health confirm that men are only half as likely to go to their GP as women and will put off seeing a doctor until their symptoms are severe. Even when they do bravely turn up at the surgery, 40% of their appointments have been made by their wives or girlfriends.

2 ☐ Trevor Jellis, a psychologist who treats stressed executives, admits to not paying enough attention to his health. 'I'm ashamed to say that as men, many of us do share the childish fantasy of being immortal,' he says. 'I was certainly guilty of that. I hadn't been to the doctor for four years when I had my first heart attack. I didn't go because I hadn't needed to, and that's precisely where I and many men

go wrong. You should not wait until then, you should have an annual health check.'

3 ☐ Jane DeVille-Almond, a practice nurse in the Midlands, recognises the problem. 'Men think that being ill is not very macho, it's a sign of weakness. So they'll create a big drama about being ill at home but they won't go public. But also doctors' surgeries are not male-friendly places. Just look around and you will see female receptionists, female nurses and women's magazines on the tables.'

4 ☐ She recently designed a project aimed at reaching the large numbers of men aged between 30 and 60 who hardly ever visited her surgery unless in an emergency. She decided that if the men wouldn't come to her, she would go to them, so she set up a clinic in the lounge bar of the Moxley Arms, a working man's pub in Walsall. The men who arrived were exactly the sort of people who need her help: men on low incomes who drink too much and eat an unhealthy diet. 'These are the men we really need to get through to. It soon became obvious that they were far more comfortable talking about their problems on home ground surrounded by their mates,' she said.

b Match the titles to the correct paragraph.

A ☐ We'll live forever

B ☐ If they don't want to come to me …

C ☐ Too late or never

D ☐ For women only?

c Find phrasal verbs which mean:

In paragraph 1

1 postpone _____ _____

2 appear _____ _____

3 support _____ _____

4 be a question of, concern _____ _____

In paragraph 4

5 establish, start _____ _____

6 communicate with sb _____ _____ (to sb)

7 Writing: Connectors

Read the 'for and against' essay. Cross out the connectors that don't fit.

> **What are the advantages and disadvantages of being a doctor?**
>
> In many countries in the world being a doctor is considered one of the most prestigious jobs there is – it is often harder to get into university to study medicine than to study anything else. [1]*But/Besides* there are advantages and disadvantages.
>
> [2]*Firstly/The main advantage* for many people is that the job itself is so important. A doctor can save lives, or can help to make people feel better. [3]*In addition/However*, in many countries doctors earn good salaries, especially if they [4]*as well/also* have a private clinic.
>
> [5]*On the other hand/Secondly* most doctors, particularly the young ones, have to work very long hours, and even top specialists are often on duty all night. [6]*But/Besides*, doctors have a lot of responsibility and stress: having to tell someone that a member of their family is dead, or seeing other people die must be a terrible experience.
>
> [7]*To sum up/At the end* I think that for anyone who likes helping other people and is good at science, a career in medicine will always be an attractive option.

Do you want to be young forever?

> 'The secret of staying young is to live honestly, eat slowly, and lie about your age.'
> *Lucille Ball, US actress*

GRAMMAR

1 CHECK WHAT YOU KNOW: Future forms

a Revise the rules. Then do exercise **b**.

Use	Example	Notes/Problems
For **future plans**, use *going to*.	*I'm going to look for a job.* *What are you going to do next summer?*	(= I've already decided.) (= What are your plans?)
For **unplanned decisions/offers/ promises**, use *will/won't* + infinitive.	*I'll answer the phone.* **A** *This case is heavy.* **B** *I'll help you./Shall I help you?*	(= you decide at this moment) NOT ~~I help you~~. ❶ If the offer is a question use *shall* with *I* or *we*. NOT ~~will~~
For **predictions**, use either *will* or *going to*.	*I think Brazil will win/are going to win.*	(= it's my opinion)
For **future arrangements**, use the **present continuous**, especially with *go, come, see, meet, leave, have* (*dinner*, etc.).	*I'm having dinner with Ann tomorrow.* *We're meeting some friends tonight.*	(= We've already booked the restaurant.) *going to* is also possible.
To say what is **possibly** going to happen, use *may/might* + **infinitive**.	*Take your umbrella. It might rain.* *Jane may not come tomorrow.*	(= it's a possibility) NOT ~~It's possible that it rains~~. (= maybe she won't come)

b Underline the correct verb form(s) in these sentences. (Sometimes two are possible.)

1 Computer scientists predict that the new virus *is going to affect/is affecting/will affect* at least two million PCs in the next two days.

2 *I may meet/I'm meeting/I'll meet* my girlfriend for dinner tonight. I've booked a table at my favourite restaurant.

3 I've decided *I change/I'm going to change/ I'm changing* my job.

4 **A** I can't get the computer to work.

  B Don't worry, *I help/I'll help/I'm helping* you.

5 Look out! *You'll hit/You're hitting/You're going to hit* your head, if you're not careful.

6 **A** Jane, I think that's your mobile ringing.

  B I'm sorry. *I'm going to switch/I'm switching/I'll switch* it off.

7 **A** What *are you doing/are you going to do/ will you do* tonight?

  B I don't know. *I'm going/I'll go/I might go* to the cinema or to a disco.

2 NEW LANGUAGE: Future continuous/ Future perfect

Complete the sentences with the verb in either the future perfect or the future continuous.

1 By the end of the year, they _____ at least a million records. (sell)

2 In the autumn they _____ their new album, which will be finished in January. (record)

3 This time tomorrow I _____ on the beach in the sun. (lie)

4 By the end of the week she _____ if she wants to have the operation or not. (decide)

5 After you've spent six months in London, I'm sure you _____ English fluently. (speak)

6 At 9 o'clock tomorrow my boyfriend _____ to Rome on business. (travel)

7 My GP said I _____ my illness by the end of the month. (get over)

8 The DJ _____ fifty songs by the time his programme finishes. (play)

9 My daughter, who is pregnant, wants to carry on working, so I _____ my grandchild. (bring up)

10 Don't worry. I'm sure we _____ the problem before the week's over. (solve)

VOCABULARY

3 Expressions with *time*

Complete the 'time' expressions.

EXAMPLE My children listen to the
Top 20 **three times** ___*a*___ **week**.

1 I never _____ **time** watching reality
shows on television. They're absolute
rubbish.

2 Don't hurry. _____ **your time**.

3 _____ **three years' time** I hope I'll
have finished university.

4 The presenter's very punctual. She always
starts her programme _____ **time**.

5 I _____ **a great time** with Jim last
night.

6 I see my family _____ **time**
_____ **time**.

7 It _____ **a long time** to drive
through London in the rush hour.

8 _____ **time** tomorrow I'll be flying
to Honolulu.

4 Science

Dolly, the first cloned animal

Complete the sentences with the correct
form of the word in brackets.

1 _____ engineering is a very
controversial issue. (gene)

2 Some _____ think we may
soon be cloning humans. (science)

3 There are _____ reasons why
we get old. (biology)

4 Researchers hope the tests will
_____ . (success)

5 My father-in-law is a _____ .
(chemistry)

6 The experiment was a _____
and he was very disappointed. (fail)

5 Computers

a Write the words to match the definitions.

1 the set of keys on a computer _____

2 the programs and other operating
material used by a computer _____

3 a piece of equipment for moving around
the screen of a computer without
touching the keys _____

4 a piece of equipment which allows a
computer to be connected to the Internet _____

5 a piece of writing created on a computer _____

6 a page or pages on the Internet which
give information _____

7 a piece of equipment used to print
information from a computer _____

8 the machinery of a computer _____

b Complete with a verb from the list.

attach download edit enter insert press save scan search

1 _____ the photo from the newspaper.

2 _____ a document to an e-mail.

3 _____ a key to start the program.

4 _____ a document so you don't lose it.

5 _____ your password before you start.

6 _____ for information on the Internet.

7 _____ a document to correct mistakes.

8 _____ information from the Internet onto your own P

9 _____ a floppy disc into the disk drive.

6 Pronunciation: the letter *y*

Circle the word with the different sound.

1 recycle   analyse   symptom   shy
2 floppy   sky   reply   deny
3 syllable   analysis   physics   psychiatrist
4 healthy   terrify   happy   easy
5 **u**niform   youth   yoga   umbrella

READING AND WRITING

7 Reading

a Read the three extracts and decide which person is the most positive about being 50.

AGE OF CONTENT?

A
Lulu,
singer

'**AS I GET OLDER** I feel more comfortable in my own skin – it's like wearing an old pair of shoes. I now know where I'm going, whereas when I was 15 all I knew about was singing and all I cared about was making a success of it. Reflecting on my life now at 50, I realize I've got everything I've ever wanted in the way of my career, health, and relationships, but what I'm still looking for is ultimate peace of mind. I want to be able to appreciate everything I've got every second of the day.

As a wife I've learnt a lot over the past ten years and I've changed in the way I give more and I'm more tolerant. As a mother I've also become more patient. A few years ago I found being a mother was very tiring.'

B
David Steel, politician

'**SINCE TURNING 50** I've become much calmer because I know I can stop working so hard. I'm a more relaxed husband to be with now because I spend more time at home and I'm also much more patient with my children. Before I had hardly any time with them.

I don't mind the physical aspects of growing old at all. That's probably because I enjoy excellent health and feel just the same as I did when I was 30: my memory's just as bad as it's always been. My children don't believe I've only got a few grey hairs on my head.

I'm one of those people who has never planned the future. My philosophy has always been to take life as it comes and I don't intend to change that now I'm 50.'

C
Margaret Forster, writer

'**MY IDEA OF A GOOD TIME** on a Saturday night has only changed very slightly over the years. It used to be staying in with a new novel and a really good apple, but now it's staying in with a new novel and a glass of wine.

I didn't feel comfortable when I was young because I was an idealist and a romantic. I used to behave spectacularly badly in my twenties. I remember once standing and shouting in the middle of Oxford Circus for no particular reason. I actually stopped the traffic! In my thirties I was too tired to have the energy to shout and by the time I was 40, thankfully I didn't want to any more.

The main reason I can be serene at 50 is that I've got the majority of things I've wanted from life, particularly in my work.'

b Answer the questions with A, B or C.

EXAMPLE
Who is glad that thay now have some direction in their life? ☐A☐

1 Who has a problem remembering things? ☐
2 Who says they enjoy staying at home on Saturday nights? ☐
3 Whose behaviour has improved? ☐
4 Who doesn't like planning the future? ☐
5 Who hasn't found everything they are looking for? ☐
6 Who thinks they are very healthy? ☐
7 Who has been married for ten years? ☐
8 Who has become more patient as a parent? ☐ ☐

c Underline any new words and try to guess them from the context. Check with a dictionary.

8 Writing: Spelling mistakes

Read the composition carefully and underline ten spelling mistakes. Write the words correctly.

What is the best age to get married?

In my opinion, there is no perfect age for a couple to get married. However, some moments are better than others to undertake this serius commitment.

Firstly, many couples get married far to young
5 when they still have not had time to enjoy their freedom as adults. This is probably the main reason for the increasing divorce rate that every country is experienceing at the moment. Secondly, a couple should get married for the right reasons. They
10 shouldn't get married just to scape from a dificult family situation. Marriing for money is also not recomended. Althought it is nice to have money, rich couples can be just as unhappy as poor ones. In fact the only really good reason for getting
15 married is when two people love each other and want to spend the rest of there lives together.

In conclusion, people should get married when they fell they are ready. Age does not matter if the time is right.

Hooked on caffeine

'The unfortunate thing about this world is that good habits are so much easier to give up than bad ones.'
W. Somerset Maugham, English writer

GRAMMAR

1 NEW LANGUAGE: Past simple, *used to, usually*?

Underline the correct verb form(s) in these sentences. (Sometimes two are possible.)

1 When I was younger I *took/used to take/was taking* medicine every time I had a cold, but now I see a homeopathic doctor.

2 Last year they *had/used to have/were having* their first hit record and now they're planning a tour.

3 My father *used to live/usually lives/was living* in France when he *met/used to meet/was meeting* my mother.

4 My grandmother *had/used to have/was having* a stroke last year.

5 My doctor *usually prescribes/used to prescribe/was prescribing* tablets for my headaches, but they don't always work.

6 When we lived in Hong Kong we often *watched/used to watch/were watching* CNN to keep in touch with the world news.

7 Nowadays a lot of teenagers *usually listen/used to listen/listened* to the Top 20 every day.

8 When my sister was pregnant, she *felt/used to feel/was feeling* sick every morning.

2 *Used to, be used to, get used to*

a Complete the sentences with the correct form of the verb in brackets.

1 My mother-in-law is used to _____ a sore throat because she has chronic pharyngitis. (have)

2 Newspapers didn't use to _____ such sensationalist articles. (print)

3 I'll have to get used to _____ with a laptop if I have to travel more. (work)

4 A lot of children always shout because they are not used to _____ quietly. (talk)

5 I never used to _____ new words in a dictionary, but now I do. (look up)

6 There didn't use to _____ cable and satellite TV in my street but now everyone has it. (be)

7 Hypochondriacs get used to _____ about their illnesses. (complain)

8 Richard didn't use to _____ his brother, but now they look almost identical. (look like)

b Look at the pictures and complete the sentences with *used to/didn't use to*, *is/isn't used to* or *get used to* + the verb in the correct form.

A before   after   B before   after

A

1 He _____ however he liked, but now he has to wear a suit. (dress)

2 Before, he _____ sleep anywhere, but now he _____ in a comfortable bed. (be able to, sleep)

3 He had to _____ early when he started work. (get up)

4 He _____ people in authority when he was a punk. (look up to)

B

1 She _____ from 9 to 5, but now she works all hours. (work)

2 She _____ very much money, but now she's a millionnaire. (have)

3 She had to _____ interviews to the press when she became famous. (give)

4 She _____ shy, but now _____ lots of people at parties. (be, meet)

VOCABULARY

3 Word formation

a Form nouns by adding the suffixes *-ility*, *-ion* and *-ment* and making any other necessary changes.

| able addict argue concentrate |
| corrupt develop embarrass expand |
| improve obsess possible replace |
| responsible restrict tense |

-ility _____ _____

_____

-ion _____ _____

_____ _____

_____ _____

_____

-ment _____ _____

_____ _____

_____

b Use a suitable noun from **a** to complete each sentence.

1 My daughter's _____ with that pop group is driving me mad.

2 I nearly died of _____ when I saw myself on TV!

3 Tom's _____ to alcohol is probably what caused his liver problems.

4 The present _____ on smoking in public places should be extended to include offices.

5 The new system isn't an _____ . In fact, it's worse.

6 Our neighbours had a terrible _____ last night. We could hear them shouting at each other.

7 Is there no _____ of changing the date of the meeting?

8 One of her good points is her _____ to adapt to different situations.

4 Adjectives and prepositions

Right ✓ or wrong ✗ ? Correct the wrong prepositions.

1 I'm fed up about always having to put away my childrens' clothes. ☐ _____

2 I'm very fond of guinea pigs. I've got two of them. ☐ _____

3 He's mad with the music of the last decade. ☐ _____

4 My mother is tired with listening to my father complaining all the time. ☐ _____

5 She's very interested on homeopathic medicine. ☐ _____

6 I'm hooked on that soap opera – it's great! ☐ _____

7 She's really keen in jogging. She does it every day. ☐ _____

8 Unfortunately my neighbour has become addicted with tranquillizers. ☐ _____

9 I was fascinated for his story – it was so interesting. ☐ _____

10 My brothers are obsessed with *Oasis*. They listen to them all the time. ☐ _____

5 Remember phrasal verbs

Complete with a verb from the list in the correct form.

| cut get (x2) give sell turn wear |

EXAMPLE Your shoes are really _worn_ **out**. You need to get some new ones.

1 It takes at least a week to _____ **over** the flu.

2 I've managed to _____ **down** from 20 cigarettes a day to 10.

3 They invited 30 people to the party, but only 10 _____ **up**.

4 The doctor told me to _____ **up** caffeine, but I'm finding it very hard.

5 **A** How are you _____ **on**?

   B Fine, just fine.

6 There are no seats left. They're _____ **out**.

READING AND WRITING

6 Reading

a Read the article once quite quickly. What's the text mainly about? Tick ✓ 1, 2, or 3.

1 Why Indian food is good for you. ☐
2 Why curry can be physically addictive. ☐
3 Why people should eat less curry. ☐

b Read the text again carefully with the glossary. Mark the sentences **T** (true) or **F** (false).

1 People who eat a lot of curry usually know that they are addicted to it. ☐
2 Your blood pressure goes up just from thinking about having a curry. ☐
3 How addictive a curry is depends on how hot it is. ☐
4 Curry is much more addictive than fish and chips. ☐
5 Only adults took part in the experiment. ☐
6 Eating *rogan josh* increases your heart beat by more than twice as much as eating fish and chips. ☐
7 People who are addicted to curry are also often addicted to chocolate. ☐
8 Curry addiction is similar to addiction to sleeping pills. ☐

Some need it hot

'CURRYHOLICS' may be more hooked on their favourite Indian dish than they realise. Researchers at Nottingham Trent University have found that eating a curry raises the heartbeat and blood pressure to a much greater extent than blander food. The result is that the bodies of 'curryholics' crave curry, and can even get satisfaction just from the anticipation of an Indian meal. Frequent consumers also develop a tolerance to curries, so they have to eat hotter and hotter dishes in order to get their 'fix'. The hotter the curry is, the more addictive it is. 'Rogan josh', a very hot lamb dish made with tomatoes, onions, garlic and ginger in addition to the usual curry spices, is the most addictive curry of all.

Professor Stephen Gray, who led the research, said: 'What we are seeing is physiological and psychological effects combining to create an addiction. Curry gives you a natural 'high' much more powerful than anything you get with traditional British foods.' In the study the researchers analysed the effects of three types of curry on 100 volunteers aged between 10 and 80. The effects were significant when compared to a control meal of fish and chips. All three curries led to a much greater increase in blood pressure and heart rate with *rogan josh* having the strongest effect: among people eating fish and chips heart rate was raised by 3.2 beats per minute, but among people eating *rogan josh* it was 6.7. Simple anticipation of a curry resulted in a similar increase in heart rate. 'In this respect it is more like an addiction to something like chocolate than to a drug' said Professor Gray. 'You cannot get a 'high' from anticipating a drug, you need to take the drug itself'.

7 Writing: An informal letter

Read the letter Angie wrote to a friend. Cross out the more formal expressions.

Dear Karen,

[1]*Thanks / Thank you* for your letter. It was [2]*very nice / great* to hear from you. [3]*I'm really looking forward / I look forward* to seeing you in the summer [4]*but / however* first there are a few things I [5]*would like / want* to ask you.

What's the weather usually like in summer in Britain? I don't really know what to pack and I [6]*haven't got / don't have* a very big suitcase.

[7]*Are you be able to / Can you* come and meet me at the airport? If not, just [8]*let me know / inform me* how to get to the station and you can [9]*pick me up / collect me* there.

[10]*One more thing / I have one more question* – how much money should I bring? Is it easy to change traveller's cheques or would it be better to bring cash?

Please write soon.

Lots of love

Debbie

LISTENING

1 A brief history of acupuncture

a **T2.1** Listen to the interview to get a general idea of what acupuncture is.

b Listen again and mark the sentences **T** (true) or **F** (false).

1 Acupuncture originated 250 years ago in China. ☐

2 Traditional Chinese medicine believes that health depends on the flow of energy in the body. ☐

3 There are 14 main acupoints in the body. ☐

4 The needles are inserted in your body where you have the pain. ☐

5 You never get any treatment on your first visit. ☐

6 You have to go once or twice a month to get results. ☐

7 Most people find that acupuncture doesn't usually hurt. ☐

8 Many people find acupuncture sessions stressful. ☐

2 The best years of my life

A ☐ C ☐ B ☐ D ☐

a **T2.2** Listen to four people talking about their age. Match them to the pictures above and write their ages.

b Listen again and match the sentences to speakers 1–4.

Which speaker(s) …

a didn't like being a teenager? ☐ ☐

b like the freedom of their present age? ☐ ☐

c would like more free time? ☐

d preferred life nine years earlier? ☐

e has noticed changes in her appearance? ☐

f thinks the best age is coming soon? ☐

PRONUNCIATION

1 Rhythm and intonation

T2.3 Listen and repeat the five sentences. Try to copy the rhythm.

2 Consonant sounds

T2.4 Go to **Vocabulary Builder 1** *p.126* in the Student's Book. Listen and repeat some of the consonants from the **English sounds** chart, and these words with the same sounds from File 2.

21 /p/ **p**rescription, G**P**
22 /b/ **b**lood, **b**iology
23 /k/ a**ch**e, **ch**ronic
24 /g/ **g**uinea pi**g**
25 /f/ **c**ough, **f**lu
26 /v/ **v**irus, sa**v**e
27 /t/ **t**reatment, **t**able**ts**
28 /d/ **d**ocument, **d**ata
29 /s/ **s**cience, **s**urgeon
30 /z/ phy**s**ical, di**zz**y
31 /ʃ/ patient, **s**pecialist
32 /ʒ/ massa**g**e, u**s**ually
33 /θ/ **th**eory, **th**roat
34 /ð/ wi**th**drawal, o**th**er
35 /tʃ/ resear**ch**, atta**ch**
36 /dʒ/ **g**enetics, a**g**e
37 /l/ **l**oad, a**ll**ergy
38 /r/ **r**est, **r**ecover
39 /w/ **w**ard, **w**ebsite
40 /j/ **y**outh, **u**sed
41 /m/ **m**ode**m**, **m**edicine
42 /n/ **n**ormally, e**n**gineer
43 /ŋ/ lo**ng**, you**ng**
44 /h/ **h**urt, **h**ypochondriac

3 Word stress

a Underline the stressed syllables.

1 allergy
2 appointment
3 fascinated
4 virus
5 biologist
6 keyboard
7 teenager
8 laboratory
9 prescription
10 tranquillizer
11 swollen
12 addicted
13 interesting
14 acupuncture
15 available

b **T2.5** Listen and repeat the words.

'Why don't you write books people can read?'
Nora Joyce (said to her husband James Joyce, the Irish novelist)

GRAMMAR

1 NEW LANGUAGE: Past simple/ Past continuous/Past perfect

Find and correct the mistake in each sentence.

1 What was you searching for on the Internet?

2 Why you had a day off last week?

3 While Julia looked round the house, her ex-husband suddenly turned up.

4 Ten minutes after she has taken the sleeping pills, she fell asleep.

5 I was downloading my e-mail when suddenly my computer was breaking down.

6 What was writing down the journalist during the interview?

7 We hadn't enough time to finish the exercise.

8 The plane already landed when I arrived at the airport to pick up my friend.

2 Past perfect simple or continuous?

Underline the correct verb form(s) in these sentences. (Sometimes both are possible.)

1 My car suddenly stopped in the middle of the motorway. It *had run out/had been running out* of petrol.

2 Last night I fainted at the concert. I *had felt/had been feeling* dizzy for a few minutes and then suddenly everything went black.

3 Yesterday James came home from school crying. He *had fallen down/had been falling down* and his knee was bleeding.

4 I started using homeopathic medicine when I had a throat infection. My GP *had treated/had been treating* me for flu and I didn't feel any better.

5 We had a terrible shock when we got back to the car park and saw that our car *had vanished/had been vanishing*!

3 Narrative tenses: Telling a story

Complete the text with a verb from the list in the correct tense.

convince forget have look make realize see send
think win write (x2)

Last September I ¹_____ up my mind to enter the Daily Telegraph's mini saga competition.

I ²_____ about entering all through the summer, and my brother finally ³_____ me that I ⁴_____ a good chance of winning, so I ⁵_____ my story and ⁶_____ it to the newspaper.

Two months later, when I ⁷_____ through the paper one morning I suddenly ⁸_____ a headline: 'Anonymous story wins'. When I read the article, I ⁹_____ that my entry ¹⁰_____ first prize but I ¹¹_____ to include my name and address in the envelope so nobody knew who ¹²_____ the story!

VOCABULARY

4 Verbs which are often confused

a Read the story. Cross out the wrong verbs.

Last week I went to my local bookshop. I was looking forward to ¹*knowing/meeting* my favourite author who was visiting the shop that day to sign books. When I saw her, I thought she ²*looked/seemed* fantastic. She had obviously ³*won/earned* a lot of money from all the books she'd written, and she was ⁴*carrying/wearing* very elegant clothes. I ⁵*hoped/waited* that she would sign my copy of the book for me, although there were a lot of other people there, and finally I was able to ⁶*tell/say* hello to her. At that moment we ⁷*noticed/realized* that we ⁸*knew/met* each other. We had been friends years ago and had shared a flat together. She wrote under a pseudonym, which is why I had never ⁹*realized/noticed* that it was her. The crowds of people ¹⁰*avoided/prevented* us from having a proper conversation, so we agreed to meet for lunch. We had a great time ¹¹*discussing/arguing* literature and I ¹²*remembered/reminded* her of when she was just a poor student!

b Match the two halves of the sentences.

1 He stole | a a music shop.
2 He robbed | b some CDs.

3 She can speak | a English fluently.
4 At the moment she's talking | b on the phone.

5 I talked to our new au pair on the phone. | a She seems very nice.
6 Our new au pair has sent us a photo. | b She looks very nice.

7 I listen to the news on the radio every day. | a Please turn the radio up.
8 I can't hear the news. | b I never buy a newspaper.

9 I hope | a my husband will forget my birthday.
10 I expect | b he'll get me a nice present.

11 'What do you want to do tonight?' | a 'I don't mind.'
12 'Sorry, I can't come tonight.' | b 'It doesn't matter.'

13 Speed cameras are used | a to avoid having an accident.
14 Drive carefully | b to prevent accidents.

15 He hadn't realized | a her wedding ring.
16 He hadn't noticed | b that she was married.

5 Pronunciation: Regular past tenses

Write the past form of the verbs in the list in the correct column according to the pronunciation of the final *-ed*.

argue avoid edit ~~hope~~ influence involve matter
prescribe press print publish realize search tend treat

d	t	/ɪd/
	hoped	

READING AND WRITING

6 Reading

a Read the mini sagas. Match the endings (A–C) to the stories.

A I am returning in three minutes.

B 'You just did,' laughed the housekeeper.

C Nobody.

---

❶ Meeting the boss

'He likes dinner at six,' she told the *maid*. 'And no beef. He has dessert in the garden. Fill the bath at eight – he goes to bed early.'

'When will I meet the master?' the maid asked as she fell over a sleeping *poodle*.

☐

---

❷ Final witness

There was total chaos. The next *witness* was walking through the courtroom doors. 'Order in the court!' shouted the *judge* as he banged the table loudly. Everyone looked at Tommy, who was sitting with his mouth open in shock. It was quite obvious now who had murdered his wife.

☐

---

❸ The end

Exhausted by jealousy, she said, 'Promise you won't open this letter for an hour. If you do, I will leave you forever.' He was *tormented* as to where she was going, but still he promised. Immediately she left he opened the letter. It said:

☐

---

b Match the highlighted words to the definitions below.

1 a woman whose job is to clean in a house or hotel _____

2 the person who decides how criminals should be punished _____

3 in great mental pain _____

4 a small dog with very curly hair _____

5 a person who sees sth happening and tells other people about it _____

c Read the stories again. Answer the questions.

Story 1 Who was the maid's master? _____

Story 2 Who was the witness? _____

Story 3 What did she do in the end? _____

7 Writing: Checking for mistakes

Check the verb forms in this story. There are ten mistakes: either the wrong tense has been used, or the wrong verb, or the form is wrong. Underline them and correct them.

. . . .

A day I'll never forget

A day I'll never forget was the day I started my final exams at university. I thought that the first exam was in the afternoon but my friend waked me up at 9 o'clock and told me to hurry as we was going to be late. The

5 exam began at 9.30.

We run all the way to the exam centre, but, unfortunately, when we were going up the steps, I fell and hurted myself. Then the exam was started. I knew I haven't studied enough but I stayed in my seat for as

10 long as possible, writing down everything I knew on the exam paper.

When I left the exam, half an hour earlier than everyone else, I meet my Professor, who asked me how it had gone. I wasn't wanting to tell him the truth so I said,

15 'Very well.' He said he had learned me everything he knew about his subject and he waited I'd get good marks. Of course I failed.

. . . .

I will survive

'I am just going out and I may be some time.'
Captain Oates' last words to Scott and his companions

GRAMMAR

1 CHECK WHAT YOU KNOW: Second and third conditionals

a Revise the rules. Then do exercises **b** and **c**.

Third conditional

Use	Example	Notes/Problems
To speculate about something that happened and how it could have been different (= a hypothetical possibility).	*If I'd seen you, I would have stopped. If we hadn't been so tired, we wouldn't have left the party so early.*	(= but I didn't see you so I didn't stop.) ❶ Don't use *would have* after if. NOT ~~if I would have seen you~~ …

b Match the sentence halves.

1 I'd have gone climbing … ☐
2 If my keys had been on the table, … ☐
3 We would have heard her … ☐
4 They'd never have seen her … ☐
5 If I'd known it was stolen, … ☐
6 If she were more friendly, … ☐
7 If you'd reminded me, … ☐
8 If it was dangerous, … ☐

a if she had shouted.
b I would talk to her more.
c I wouldn't have bought it.
d if the weather hadn't been so bad.
e if she hadn't been wearing a red scarf.
f I wouldn't do it.
g I wouldn't have forgotten.
h I would have noticed them.

c Complete the sentences with the verbs in the correct tense.

1 If he hadn't broken his leg, he

_____ on our last trip. (come)

2 If I _____ young children, I'd

go out more often. (not have)

3 If the mountain wasn't so dangerous, more

people _____ to climb it. (try)

4 We wouldn't have got lost if the weather

_____ so bad. (not be)

5 I _____ the number if I'd

known it was important. (write down)

6 They'd love to come if they

_____ so busy. (not be)

2 NEW LANGUAGE: *Should/shouldn't have*

Quickly read the story. Then complete it with *should/ shouldn't have* + the verb in brackets in the correct form.

Never again …

Somehow, I knew the holiday was going to be a disaster. First, I [1] _____ (choose) to go skiing, I [2] _____ (go) to the beach instead, as what I really needed was to relax. On the morning of my flight I got up really late. I [3] _____ (set) my alarm clock earlier. I had also meant to pack the night before, but I went to a party until late. Of course I [4] _____ (go) to that party – and above all I [5] _____ (drink) so much – my head was aching terribly. So, there I was, two hours before the plane was due to take off, throwing things in my suitcase. Yes, I know I [6] _____ (pack) the night before. Surprisingly, my car started first time, but once I got on the motorway, the traffic was terrible. I [7] _____ (take) the underground. On my first morning skiing I started off quite slowly, but then I thought I'd be a bit more ambitious. It's easy to say now, but I [8] _____ (be) more careful. Anyway, I lost control of my skis, went straight into a tree, and broke my leg. I spent the rest of the week in hospital!

VOCABULARY

3 Strong adjectives

a Complete the chart.

Normal adjectives	Strong adjectives
1 *tired*	exhausted
2	filthy
3	terrified
4	tiny
5	fascinated
6	freezing
7	hideous
8	devastated
9	horrified
10	amazed

b Complete the dialogues with *absolutely* and a strong adjective.

EXAMPLE

   A The mountain looked very big.

   B Yes, it was *absolutely* *enormous* .

1 **A** Her son's very clever, isn't he?

   B Yes, people say he's _____

    _____ .

2 **A** Were you pleased with your exam results?

   B Yes, I was _____ _____ .

3 **A** She was really angry with the press about that article.

   B Yes, and her boyfriend was _____

    _____ .

4 **A** Are you hungry?

   B Hungry? I'm _____ _____ .

5 **A** The weather forecast was right! They said it was going to be really hot today.

   B Yes, it's _____ _____ , isn't it?

4 Remember words from the text

Write the words for the definitions below.

1	a high wall of rock	cl_____
2	a thick strong cord used for climbing, etc.	ro_____
3	a snow storm	bl_____
4	pull something with difficulty	dr_____
5	a vehicle without wheels used for travelling on snow	sl_____
6	try hard to do something very difficult	str_____

5 Pronunciation: Diphthongs

Write two words under each sound picture.

blame   boiling   choice   coward   delighted   furious   lower   mountain   nearer   really   rope   scared   tiny   tour   wear   weight

blame   _____   _____

_____   _____   _____

_____   _____   _____

_____   _____   _____

_____   _____

_____   _____

READING AND WRITING

6 Reading

a Read the article and find out where Jochen Hemmleb thought he would find the body of Andrew Irvine.

Mallory and Irvine: Did they make it to the top?

On June 8, 1924, George Mallory and Andrew Irvine began the final stage of their attempt to be the first to conquer Everest. But when they were only 267m from the top, they vanished into the mists, never to be seen again.

For almost a decade after they were last seen, no one had a clue what had happened to them. Had they reached the top and then died on the way down, thus being the first men to climb Everest? Or did they die before getting there?

In 1933, during the next British Everest expedition, a climber found an ice axe high on the Northeast Ridge at 9000m. The axe

had a characteristic identification mark, but at the time nobody recognised it. Thirty years later, in 1962 one of Irvine's brothers found an old walking stick belonging to Irvine. It had identical markings, so the ice axe must have been Irvine's. However, his body could not be found.

In April 1999 Jochen Hemmleb, a world expert on the history of Everest expeditions, set out with a team of men to try to find out the truth about what had happened to them.

Hemmleb already knew that a Chinese climber, Wang Hongbao, had found the body of an Englishman in 1975 a short walk from the Chinese expedition's camp 6. Wang had told this to a Japanese climber

in 1979, but was unable to give accurate details as he was killed by an avalanche the next day. Hemmleb, however, decided that the only way to confirm this information was to find the 1975 Chinese camp 6 and search the area in a 20 minute radius around the camp. 'Find the camp,' said Hemmleb, 'and you'll find Irvine.'

Finding the Chinese camp 6 was not easy because the Chinese had not given much information about the 1975 climb. Hemmleb had to work out the exact location by comparing photos of different expeditions' camp 6s and was not surprised to find it in an area well away from the path climbers use today.

b Read the text again and choose the best answer.

1 Mallory and Irvine
   a were the first men to climb Everest.
   b died before they reached the top of Everest.
   c disappeared when they were near the top of Everest.

2 The ice axe was almost definitely Irvine's because
   a it was found near his body.
   b his brother identified it.
   c it had the same mark as on another of his possessions.

3 A Chinese climber found the body of an Englishman
   a in 1979.
   b near camp 6.
   c the day before he was killed by an avalanche.

4 Hemmleb knew where the Chinese camp 6 was because
   a the Chinese authorities had told him.
   b a Japanese climber had told him.
   c he calculated it by himself.

c Underline any words you didn't know and guess their meaning. Check with a dictionary.

You will find out what happened next when you do Listening 2 on page 33.

7 Writing: Using prepositions

Complete the composition with prepositions from the list.

for (x2)   from (x2)   in (x2)   of   through

Why do people do risk sports?

Although I don't do any risk sports myself, I admire people who do them. But why do they risk their lives?

I think the main reason [1]_____ doing risk sports is that they provide an escape [2]_____ everyday life, especially for a person who is shut [3]_____ an office all week. One possible way [4]_____ escaping is to go mountain climbing, hang-gliding or bungee jumping. The excitement and physical thrill they get [5]_____ one jump will stay with them [6]_____ the week until the following weekend when they can do it again.

Some people do risk sports to experience new feelings and emotions; others are searching [7]_____ the ultimate excitement. But whatever the reason why people take part [8]_____ risk sports, it is clear they are becoming more and more popular.

Divorced, beheaded, died …

'History is the sum total of the things that could have been avoided.'

Konrad Adenauer, German politician

GRAMMAR

1 CHECK WHAT YOU KNOW: Deduction about the present: *must/might/can't be*

a Revise the rules. Then do exercise **b**.

Use	Example	Notes/Problems
Use *must* + **infinitive** to say that you're sure something is logically true.	*He must be out. There's no answer.* *They must have a lot of money. They've got a huge house.*	❗ Don't confuse with *must* for obligation, e.g. *I must go to the bank.* Remember, the opposite of *He must be out* is *He can't be out.* NOT ~~He mustn't be out.~~
Use *might* + **infinitive** to say that something is possibly true.	*They might be Spanish or Italian – I'm not sure.* *She might be working tonight. She sometimes works on Friday evenings.*	You can also use *could* instead of *might*.
Use *can't* + **infinitive** to say that you're sure something is impossible.	*It can't be true. I don't believe it.* *He can't be in. The lights aren't on.*	

b Match the sentences.

1 The computer's not working. ☐
2 John smokes 40 cigarettes a day. ☐
3 This film must be good. ☐
4 This bill can't be right. ☐
5 Your trip sounds wonderful. ☐
6 He can't be serious. ☐
7 It's a bit late to phone. ☐
8 I wonder why he hasn't arrived. ☐
9 Do you think that's Martha? ☐

a You must be really looking forward to it.
b He must be pulling my leg.
c They might be in bed.
d He might be trying to park.
e It can't be switched on.
f It might be. It looks like her.
g It can't be very good for him.
h We hardly ordered anything.
i It's got some great actors in it.

2 NEW LANGUAGE: Deduction about the past

Write a sentence for each situation with *must have, might have* or *can't have*.

EXAMPLES

I can't find my homework. (leave it at home or on the bus)
I might have left it at home or on the bus.

Jane's got a new car. (sell the old one)
She *must have sold the old one.*

1 Sarah's nose looks completely different. (have plastic surgery)
   She _____ .

2 James is back at work. (illness be very serious)
   His _____ .

3 Those football fans look very happy. (win the match)
   Their team _____ .

4 There was a fire in the school last night. (drop a cigarette or a match)
   Someone _____ .

5 Why aren't they here yet? They know the way very well. (get lost)
   They _____ .

6 He didn't answer the telephone. (be in the garden or in the shower)
   He _____ .

VOCABULARY

3 History and politics

Do the quiz.

HISTORY AND POLITICS

PART 1

1 Who won the American Civil War?
 a) The Union Army
 b) The Confederate Army

2 Who is the heir to the British throne after Prince William?
 a) Prince Andrew **b)** Prince Harry

3 How many of Henry VIII's wives were executed?
 a) two **b)** three

4 Who surrendered at the Battle of Waterloo?
 a) Napoleon **b)** Wellington

5 Denmark, Belgium and Morocco are … .
 a) Republics **b)** Monarchies

6 What is the head of the Swedish Government called?
 a) the President
 b) the Prime Minister

PART 2 **What do you call …**

7 a person who is legally a member of a country? c_____

8 a country where many different races live? m_____-e_____

9 a plan of action chosen by a government? p_____

10 what soldiers may do when they've lost a battle? r_____ a_____

SCORE ____ /10

4 Remember words from the text

Match the sentences. Check you can remember what the **bold** words mean.

1 Jack's **infatuated** with her. ☐
2 Your efforts are **doomed** to failure. ☐
3 She was **betrayed** by her best friend. ☐
4 My grandmother died in 1963. ☐
5 You should **get rid of** that car. ☐
6 I'm sure she killed him. ☐
7 I want to **show off** my new car. ☐
8 He's very **naive**. ☐
9 Be careful with that rose. ☐
10 This skirt doesn't fit. ☐

a It's dangerous.
b He still believes in Father Christmas.
c It's got **thorns**.
d She's **guilty**.
e You'll never succeed.
f I've just bought it.
g She told her husband she was unfaithful.
h It's too tight at the **waist**.
i She's **buried** in Denmark.
j He can't think of anything else.

5 Use your dictionary: Checking pronunciation

Look up these words in your dictionary and check the meaning. Then look at the phonetics to see how they are pronounced and cross out a silent consonant in each one.

1 handkerchief   6 palm
2 dumb   7 duvet
3 yoghurt   8 debt
4 knight   9 fasten
5 receipt   10 whole

Elizabeth 1

– A queen with 'the heart and stomach of a king'

ELIZABETH 1 was the daughter of Henry VIII and Anne Boleyn and she reigned from 1558 until her death in 1603. Elizabeth was loved by her people and her forty-five year reign was in many ways 'a golden age' for England. It was the age of Shakespeare and the discovery of the New World.

When the Spanish Armada, the fleet sent by the Catholic King of Spain King Philip II to invade England in 1588, was approaching the English coast, Elizabeth made a passionate speech to encourage her soldiers. She said, 'I know I have the body of a weak and feeble woman, but I have the heart and stomach of a king, and a king of England too.' The Spanish invasion was unsuccessful and Elizabeth was confirmed as one of the most popular monarchs Britain has ever had.

But Elizabeth was anything but weak and feeble. In fact, writers of the time recorded many incidents of her being extremely strong and aggressive. One day when she got angry with her secretary she threw a slipper at him and hit him in the face, and on another occasion she hit one of her ministers who had offended her.

Elizabeth must have been very vain. A French visitor to England when she was old said, 'When anyone speaks of her beauty she says she was never beautiful but she speaks of her beauty as often as she can.' However, it is difficult to know what Elizabeth really looked like, because she did not personally pose for many of her portraits. She banned the showing of any portraits which showed her as ugly.

Elizabeth was one of the cleanest women in England at that time. She was proud of the fact that she had a bath *once* every three months! One of her ministers was amazed to discover that she had four baths a year 'whether she needed it or not'.

Although she had admirers Elizabeth never married or had children. When people suggested that she should marry she answered, 'I have already joined myself in marriage to a husband, namely the kingdom of England. Do not blame me for the lack of children, for every one of you are children of mine.'

READING AND WRITING

6 Reading

a Read the text and mark the sentences **T** (true) or **F** (false).

1 Britain was defeated by the Spanish. ☐

2 Elizabeth was loved by her people. ☐

3 She was not physically strong. ☐

4 She didn't care whether she was beautiful or not. ☐

5 Most of her portraits were painted from life. ☐

6 She didn't like some of her portraits. ☐

7 At that time people didn't use to wash often. ☐

8 Elizabeth never wanted to get married. ☐

b Look at the highlighted words and try to guess their meaning. Check with a dictionary.

7 Writing: A biography

Use the prompts to write a short biography of Mervyn Hudson. You can add words and change the verb forms but don't change any of the other words.

1 born/3rd April 1929/Bristol/south-west England

_____

_____

2 Second World War/parents send him away/stay/friends/country

_____

_____

3 leave school/sixteen/get/job/civil servant

_____

4 work twenty years/retire/1964

_____

5 marry/1953/three children

_____

6 today/eight grandchildren/enjoy gardening/reading

_____

_____

LISTENING

1 What should he have done?

a T3.1 Listen to Manolo, a Spanish businessman, talking about a frightening experience. What happened?

b Listen again and underline eight more mistakes in this summary of the story.

. . . .

Manolo and his boss, Jesús, went to <u>San Francisco</u> on holiday. One morning they hired jet-skis because they were both strong swimmers. But while Jesús was having a swim, his jet-ski floated away. It was a serious situation because, although they were quite near the beach, the sea was very rough and there were piranhas. Manolo tried to rescue him but he also lost his jet-ski. After hanging on to the rocks for an hour they were both rescued by lifeguards. Manolo said later that he only tried to save Jesús because he was his boss.

. . . .

2 Mallory and Irvine part 2

a Read the text about Mallory and Irvine on page 29 again.

b T3.2 Now listen to part of a programme about the Mallory and Irvine research expedition in May 1999. Whose body did they find? How did they identify it?

c Listen again and put the events in the correct order.

A Conred Anker found another body of a climber. ☐

B They found an old Chinese oxygen cylinder. ☐

C The expedition left camp 5. ☐

D They identified the body. ☐

E Some of them found a graveyard of dead climbers. ☐

F They reached the present camp 6. ☐

PRONUNCIATION

1 Intonation

a T3.3 Repeat the second person's responses. Copy the intonation.

b T3.4 Respond to the sentences with an appropriate expression from the list. Use expressive intonation.

No!   Really?   You're joking!   How annoying!   What a pity!
How awful!   That's great!   Wow!

---

2 Contractions

T3.5 Practise the weak or contracted form of *have*. Listen and repeat the sentences. Try to get the rhythm right.

3 Word stress

a Underline the stressed syllables.

1 exhausted	5 brilliant	9 monarchy	13 parliament
2 hideous	6 amazed	10 revolution	14 political
3 petrified	7 horrified	11 surrender	15 republic
4 enormous	8 delighted	12 dictatorship	16 government

b T3.6 Listen and repeat the words.

33

Clothes to die for

'Fashion is what one wears oneself.
What other people wear is unfashionable.'
Oscar Wilde, Irish writer

GRAMMAR

1 CHECK WHAT YOU KNOW: Adjectives

a Revise the rules. Then do exercise **b**.

Use	Example	Notes/Problems
To describe nouns or noun phrases.	*It's a huge house.* *She's got very expressive eyes.* *I think the red one is nicer than the blue one.*	Adjectives go before nouns NOT ~~a house huge.~~ Never add an *s* to make the plural. You can't use an adjective without a noun. Add *one/ones.* NOT ~~the red~~
Use **a comparative adjective** + ***than*** to compare two people or things. Use ***the*** + **a superlative adjective** to express maximums or minimums.	*His car's bigger than mine.* *This bag's heavier than that one.* *It's the highest mountain in the world.* *This is the easiest exercise.* *My new flat's more modern than yours.* *She's the most unselfish person I know.*	Form comparatives of one-syllable adjectives by adding *-er*, and superlatives + *-est*. For two-syllable adjectives ending *-y*, change to *-ier/-iest*, e.g. *heavy* – *heavier* – *the heaviest*. For other adjectives put *more/most* before the adjective, e.g. ***more*** *modern* – *the* ***most*** *modern*.
Use (*not*) ***as*** + **adjective** + ***as*** to compare two people or things. Use ***the same as*** to say that they're the same.	*It's not as far as I thought.* *Your cooking is as good as my mother's.* *Her bag's the same as mine.*	

b Cross out the wrong form.

1 A Which shirt do you like?

  B I think I prefer *the red/the red one*.

2 Sue's wearing *a skirt very old-fashioned/a very old-fashioned skirt*.

3 My dress is *looser/more loose* than yours.

4 That blouse doesn't fit you *as well than/as well as* the other one.

5 These gloves are *too tight/too tights*.

6 A tracksuit is the *more comfortable/most comfortable* thing to wear at weekends.

7 Those jeans aren't *enough big/big enough* for you.

8 That's one of *the most pretty/the prettiest* dressing-gowns I've ever seen.

9 She's wearing the same jacket *as/than* you.

10 These shoes are *too high/too much high* for me.

11 His new film is *more boring/boringer* than his last one.

12 Have we got *food enough/enough food* for the party?

2 NEW LANGUAGE: Adjective order

Right ☑ or wrong ☒? Correct the wrong sentences.

1 There was an awful old comedy on TV last night. ☐

2 I heard some classical beautiful guitar music last night on the radio. ☐

3 My granny likes wearing traditional wool skirts in the winter. ☐

4 I threw away those grey hideous trousers of yours last week. ☐

5 I always go to that restaurant because of the good-looking young waiter. ☐

6 We rented an old big country cottage for our holiday last year. ☐

7 My brother is going to buy some suede blue shoes for his birthday. ☐

8 We're going to get a big new monitor for the computer. ☐

9 She wore her silk red dress for the party. ☐

10 Why do you never wear that cotton lovely purple jumper I gave you? ☐

3 *The ... the ...*

Rewrite the sentences. Use *the ... the ...* and comparative adjectives.

EXAMPLE

If a coat is good quality, it'll last a long time.
The better quality a coat is, the longer it will last.

1 If a mountain is high, it's risky to climb.
The _____

2 If your lifestyle is healthy, you'll live a long time.
The _____

3 If a skirt is short, you have to be slim to wear it.
The _____

4 If you speak fast, it's difficult to understand you.
The _____

5 If you work hard, I'll pay you more.
The _____

6 If a school is big it's impersonal.
The _____

VOCABULARY

4 Clothes wordsearch

Find 14 different words for clothes in the grid. They can be horizontal (left to right or right to left) and vertical (top to bottom or the other way round).

E	J	T	R	I	H	S	T	A	E	W	S
D	R	E	S	S	I	N	G	G	O	W	N
J	E	V	S	M	E	O	R	A	W	O	S
L	A	D	N	A	S	T	I	E	A	L	Y
H	A	N	D	K	E	R	C	H	I	E	F
D	P	Y	J	A	M	A	S	P	S	B	S
T	S	E	V	T	R	I	K	S	T	N	E
B	L	O	U	S	E	N	D	R	C	A	V
N	S	L	I	P	P	E	R	S	O	S	O
B	T	R	I	H	S	R	A	P	A	C	L
C	T	R	A	C	K	S	U	I	T	R	G

5 Clothes idioms

Complete the sentences with a verb from the list.

dress up   fit   get changed   get dressed   hang up
match   suit   try on

1 You'll have to _____ _____ if you want to come out with me. You can't go in jeans.

2 If you don't _____ your clothes _____ they look a mess.

3 I didn't buy the suit because the trousers didn't _____ me properly. They were too small.

4 Those trousers really _____ you. You look great!

5 On cruise ships you have to _____ _____ in smart clothes for dinner.

6 I was trying to find a shirt to _____ the trousers, but I couldn't.

7 Before I buy new clothes I always _____ them _____ in the changing rooms.

8 I always _____ _____ before I have breakfast. I hate eating in pyjamas.

6 Fashion and buying clothes

Write words for the definitions.

1 a lower price than usual   **d**_____

2 a book or magazine showing all the things you can buy   **c**_____

3 you do this when aren't really thinking of buying anything   **w**_____-**s**_____

4 something you managed to buy very cheaply **b**_____

5 a large shop divided into sections
d_____ **s**_____

6 not formal (clothes)   **c**_____

7 e.g. a Chanel suit, an Armani sweater
d_____ **c**_____

8 a time when shops sell things more cheaply than usual   **s**_____

READING AND WRITING

7 Reading

a Quickly read though the six paragraphs and find out which item of clothing Rebecca Martin had a problem with and why.

WHY DID I WEAR THAT?

A ☐ I only wore them once, and that ended up costing me a lot, not only financially but also because of my embarrassment. I wore them to go shopping with my mother in Manchester, and as I walked around Kendals department store I felt as if I was the slimmest person alive.

B ☐ My mother was queueing for the coffees, so I tried to get her attention. When she saw what had happened to my trousers she couldn't stop laughing. She helped me out of the café, walking directly behind me while trying to hold my trousers together. We went straight to the fashion department where she bought me a new pair of trousers, this time size 10!

C ☑ I fell in love with my red velvet trousers the first time I saw them. They were a size 8 and, as I am usually a size 10, I never thought they would fit me. But I was determined to try, so I held my stomach in while the shop assistant tried to pull up the zip.

D ☐ After looking round the store for half an hour we went into the café and Mum told me to get a table while she got some coffees. I found an empty table but as I was sitting down I heard something rip and when I felt behind me, I realised that they had completely split apart. I felt myself go red as other shoppers had heard the noise and were looking at me.

E ☐ When I took them home my mum and my sisters thought they were awful. They said they were far too tight and hated the disgusting orange-red colour. I began to think I might have made a fashion mistake, but I had bought the trousers so I was determined to wear them.

F ☐ They were definitely a size too small – in fact they were the tightest trousers I had ever worn – but the shop assistant said they looked great so I bought them. Looking back on it now I think I had lost all sense of reality.

b Number the paragraphs in the correct order.

c Underline any new words and guess the meaning from the context. Check with a dictionary.

8 Writing: Physical descriptions

Look at the pictures and complete the descriptions.

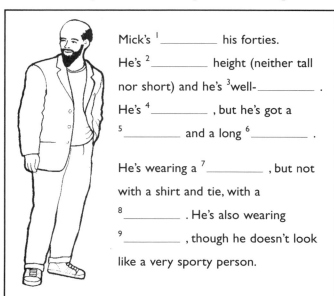

Mick's ¹_____ his forties.

He's ²_____ height (neither tall

nor short) and he's ³well-_____ .

He's ⁴_____ , but he's got a

⁵_____ and a long ⁶_____ .

He's wearing a ⁷_____ , but not

with a shirt and tie, with a

⁸_____ . He's also wearing

⁹_____ , though he doesn't look

like a very sporty person.

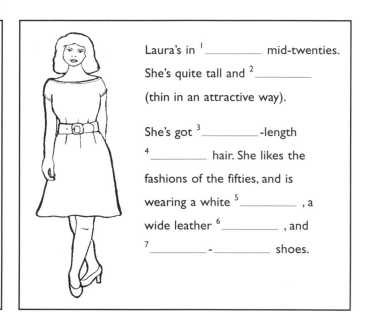

Laura's in ¹_____ mid-twenties.

She's quite tall and ²_____

(thin in an attractive way).

She's got ³_____-length

⁴_____ hair. She likes the

fashions of the fifties, and is

wearing a white ⁵_____ , a

wide leather ⁶_____ , and

⁷_____-_____ shoes.

Why men don't iron

GRAMMAR

1 CHECK WHAT YOU KNOW: *the*

Write *the* where necessary.

¹_____ last week I went shopping after ²_____ work to buy a new dress for a party I'm going to ³_____ next month. I love ⁴_____ parties. They're a good excuse for buying ⁵_____ new clothes and there's always ⁶_____ possibility that you might meet ⁷_____ interesting people. On ⁸_____ evening of ⁹_____ party, I took a long time getting dressed. I felt great wearing my new dress. But as soon as I walked through ¹⁰_____ door I saw a girl wearing exactly ¹¹_____ same dress. I nearly cried.

When I told my boyfriend he said it was ¹²_____ most ridiculous thing he'd ever heard. Of course, ¹³_____ men don't understand about ¹⁴_____ clothes, because they never notice what ¹⁵_____ people are wearing anyway.

2 NEW LANGUAGE: *wish*

a Underline the correct verb form in these sentences.

1 I wish I *didn't buy/hadn't bought* that dress. It looks awful!

2 I wish my doctor *gave/would give* me something for my allergy. I can't stop sneezing!

3 I wish I *lived/would live* somewhere where it didn't rain so much!

4 Jack wishes he *hadn't argued/didn't argue* with his girlfriend. Now she wants to cancel the wedding.

5 I wish the government *did/would do* something about the increasing crime rate. It's not safe to go out at night these days.

6 Now he wishes he *didn't tell/hadn't told* that joke. Nobody got it.

7 I wish I *didn't have to/wouldn't have to* work so hard. I need more free time.

8 They wish they *bought/had bought* the house when they had the opportunity. Now it's too late.

b Complete the article using a suitable form of the verbs in brackets.

No regrets?

If I could live my life all over again there are many things I would change. First of all, I wish I ¹_____ (not get married) so young. My wife doesn't like travelling, so I wish I ²_____ (travel) more before I met her. We don't have a very active social life and I must admit I wish we ³_____ (go out) more, and most of all, I wish sometimes my wife ⁴_____ (turn off) the television and talk to me more.

We only had one child, a daughter. I wish we ⁵_____ (have) more children when we were younger. Our daughter now lives in Canada so we hardly ever see her. I wish she ⁶_____ (live) nearer. She's married but hasn't got any children yet. I wish she ⁷_____ (have) a baby soon because I would love to be a grandfather.

And as for this house, well, I wish we ⁸_____ (buy) a house in the country when we had the chance. Our bedroom looks straight out onto a factory. I wish the local government ⁹_____ (knock it down) and build a park there instead. They have been promising to do that for years.

VOCABULARY

3 The changing roles of men and women

Complete the crossword.

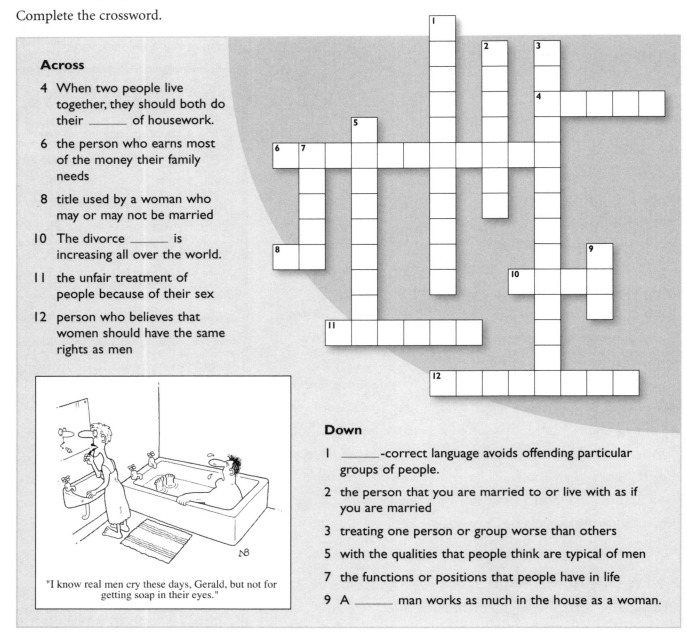

Across

4 When two people live together, they should both do their _____ of housework.

6 the person who earns most of the money their family needs

8 title used by a woman who may or may not be married

10 The divorce _____ is increasing all over the world.

11 the unfair treatment of people because of their sex

12 person who believes that women should have the same rights as men

"I know real men cry these days, Gerald, but not for getting soap in their eyes."

Down

1 _____-correct language avoids offending particular groups of people.

2 the person that you are married to or live with as if you are married

3 treating one person or group worse than others

5 with the qualities that people think are typical of men

7 the functions or positions that people have in life

9 A _____ man works as much in the house as a woman.

4 Adjectives of personality

Write the adjective of personality to match the definition.

What do you call a person who …?

1 only thinks about him/herself   s_____

2 is proud of their own appearance   v_____

3 wants what others have got   j_____

4 behaves in an adult way   m_____

5 thinks of others before he/she acts c_____

6 never betrays their partner   f_____

7 is aware of other people's feelings s_____

8 likes keeping things in order   o_____

5 Negative prefixes

Add a negative prefix to make the opposites.

1 __imaginative   6 __responsible

2 __mature   7 __sociable

3 __ambitious   8 __tidy

4 __efficient   9 __logical

5 __organized   10 __patient

6 Pronunciation

Underline the stress on the adjectives above. Practise saying them.

READING AND WRITING

7 Reading

a Read the article and complete the gaps with *men* or *women*.

FOOTBALL
divides the sexes

The day when England failed to qualify for the World Cup was a memorable one. But while most ¹_____ were shouting insults and calling for the England coach to resign, a far gentler sound was also heard: a collective sigh of relief from millions of ²_____ .

Everybody knows that ³_____ and sport go together – and it's a relationship that most ⁴_____ neither share nor understand. Most ⁵_____ can't work out why their ⁶_____ get so excited about this fairly normal sport or why some physically strong individuals should earn such huge amounts of money. To most ⁷_____ , however, football is a complicated, skilful game which they've played themselves for years. Saturdays without football would have no meaning.

   Football threatens some ⁸_____ – partly because it shows them they might not be the most important thing in ⁹_____'s lives and partly because they consider it such a waste of time. How can you respect ¹⁰_____ who spend 10 hours a week shouting insults at the television screen? It's an inactive, passive pastime which has little to do with the outside world – one reason why ¹¹_____ find it so frustrating.

Glossary	
sigh of relief	make a sound to show that a pain or worry has gone
skilful	needing ability
pastime	hobby, sth you enjoy doing

b Read the article again with the glossary. Tick ✓ the reasons why, according to the article, women don't like football.

1 Because the English team never qualifies for the World Cup. ☐

2 Because it's too complicated to understand. ☐

3 Because men think it's more important than their partners. ☐

4 Because matches take a very long time. ☐

5 Because it's totally unrelated to real life. ☐

6 Because they think footballers are overpaid. ☐

8 Writing: Correcting mistakes

Read the note from Sally to her husband. Cross out *one* extra word in each line.

> Jim,
> 1 Just a couple of things I forgot to tell ~~to~~ you
> 2 that you need to do them while I'm away.
> 3 I left some of clothes in the washing machine.
> 4 Could you to hang them up on the line?
> 5 Then the plants that they are in the living room need
> 6 to be watered, but not too much often, only once
> 7 every two days. Last thing, the children are being invited
> 8 to a party after the school on Thursday. You need to
> 9 pick them up from the Sally's house at about 7.30, OK?
> 10 I'll try to phone you as soon as I will arrive in Glasgow.
>   Speak to you later this evening.
>   Love, Louise

A question of taste

'A doctor can bury his mistakes, but an architect can only advise his client to plant vines.'
Frank Lloyd Wright, US architect

GRAMMAR

1 NEW LANGUAGE: Countable and uncountable

a Write the words from the list in the correct column in the chart.

advice business chocolate clothes furniture glass hair iron ~~jeans~~ luck news paper people police politics toast weather wood work

ALWAYS PLURAL	UNCOUNTABLE	COUNTABLE or UNCOUNTABLE
jeans		

b Write a noun and a verb from the boxes in each sentence. Make sure the verb is in the correct form.

Nouns
advice money furniture toast jeans clothes people hair

Verbs
suit match mean look be help get need

1 The new _____ in the living room
   _____ great! I love your new sofa.

2 Those _____ _____ you.
   Are they Levi's?

3 My _____ _____ cutting.
   I must make an appointment at the hairdresser's.

4 It's great talking to you. Your _____
   always _____ me solve my problems.

5 She's very fashion conscious. Her
   _____ always _____ her shoes.

6 The _____ _____ burnt this
   morning so I didn't eat it.

7 The _____ I'll earn in my new job
   _____ I'll be able to buy my own flat.

8 We love going to France. The _____
   _____ really friendly.

2 *Have something done*

Complete the sentences using *have* (in the correct form/ tense) + object + the verbs in brackets.

EXAMPLE
   My car broke down last week so I had to _____ . (repair)
   My car broke down last week so I had to *have it repaired.*

1 I _____
   at the health centre yesterday. (my blood pressure/check)

2 Jim is _____
   tomorrow. (his new computer/deliver)

3 How often _____
   these days? (your hair/cut)

4 You're sitting very close to the TV. _____
   _____ recently? (your eyes/test)

5 I'm staying with my in-laws this week as I _____
   _____ .
   (my house/redecorate)

6 Have you ever thought of _____
   _____ ? (portrait/paint)

VOCABULARY

3 Houses and decoration

a Circle the word which is different. Why?

1 bedside table   chest of drawers   wardrobe   oven

2 block of flats   porch   detached house   terraced house

3 dishwasher   sink   washbasin   washing machine

4 fence   hedge   path   wall

5 cosy   relaxing   stylish   impersonal

6 radiator   heater   bookcase   fireplace

7 hang up   put away   tidy up   turn on

8 plant pot   curtain   rug   fridge

b Write the missing consonants.

1 the top surface of the inside of a room   __ei__i__ __

2 very old and therefore unusual and valuable   a__ __i__ue

3 a pipe through which smoke is carried out of a building   __ __i__ __e__

4 a hard flat area at the side of a road for people to walk on   __a__e__e__ __

5 a door in a fence or wall   __a__e

6 a more informal word for toilet   __oo

7 you walk on this to cross a piece of land   __a__ __

c Look at pictures 1–5 and complete the phrases.

1 **A** This light doesn't work.

 B Perhaps you need to _____ .

2 The bath's overflowing! Can you _____ ?

3 Dinner's nearly ready. Could you _____ , please?

4 I've just ironed your shirt. Could you _____ in the wardrobe?

5 Don't forget to _____ when you leave the house.

4 Adjectives: Suffixes

Add a suffix to the words in the list to make adjectives. Write them in the correct place in the table.

comfort danger enjoy fashion help history luxury origin practice religion success use			
-ous			
-able	*comfortable*		
-al			
-ful			

5 Remember phrasal verbs

Complete the sentences with a phrasal verb from the list in the correct form.

carry on   go with   put away   put out   put up with run away   run out of   show off

1 I'm sorry I interrupted you. Please

 _____ .

2 When the robber saw the police car, he

 _____ .

3 She's so proud of her new boyfriend she wants to

 _____ him _____ .

4 I'm afraid you can't have a sandwich. We've

 _____ bread.

5 If you don't _____ your cigarette you'll

 have to leave. This is a non-smoking area.

6 I can't _____ this noise any more.

 I'm going to call the police.

7 If you haven't got time to tidy your room, at least

 _____ all those books and papers.

8 I don't like that sofa. It doesn't _____

 the rest of the furniture at all.

READING AND WRITING

6 Reading

a Read the whole article quickly once to get the general meaning. Then write a word in each gap.

Feng shui in the car

Feng shui, usually concerned with the comfort of people in their own homes, is now being recommended to drivers to help reduce stress and aggression in the car.

Gina Lazenby, who has studied the Chinese philosophy of controlling the earth's natural energy waves, says motorists should look at the ¹_____ of their car, ²_____ they have inside it, and where they ³_____ .

Drivers with red cars tend to drive more aggressively, because it is a bright, passionate colour. Old people prefer blues, browns and greys, which are calmer and relaxing to the mood of the driver. Drivers of yellow cars are friendly people, drivers of white cars are careful because the colour shows they want to be noticed, while drivers of black cars tend to be formal and correct.

Feng shui is very important inside the car too, according to Ms Lazenby. 'Don't fill it with rubbish which will break your concentration. Don't have things lying about that can annoy you, like a parking ticket you don't think you should pay. If you do have anything in view, make sure it's a picture of your partner or loved ones. Looking at an image of someone you really care about is relaxing and helps with smooth, safe driving.'

She also says you should not park your car outside your front door as this will stop positive energy from entering your house. 'If you do park outside, make sure it is to one side so that visitors can walk right up to the entrance.'

However, few motorists, we spoke to, believe in the values of *feng shui*. Clive Steadman, who drives a red van, admitted that he was lucky if he got up to 45kph. 'The van's falling apart, but that's got nothing to do with my stress levels or energy flows.'

b Read the text again slowly and mark the sentences **T** (true) or **F** (false).

1 Drivers should use *feng shui* to help them relax when they're driving. ☐

2 *Feng shui* offers drivers advice in three specific areas. ☐

3 People choose yellow cars because they want to be noticed. ☐

4 If the inside of your car is a mess, it will stop you from concentrating. ☐

5 Having pictures or photos in your car is very distracting. ☐

6 When you park you should make sure not to block the entrance to your house. ☐

7 Most drivers don't take *feng shui* seriously. ☐

8 Clive's red van makes him drive more aggressively. ☐

7 Writing: Using headings

a Divide the composition into five paragraphs (introduction, three main paragraphs, and conclusion).

b Write headings for the three main paragraphs.

1 _____

2 _____

3 _____

· ·

Write a report about what young people in your country do in their free time.

Most young people in my country don't have much free time during the week – they are usually studying or working. However, they are normally free at weekends and students especially have very long summer holidays. In the morning or
5 evening most young people probably listen to music, either before or after work/school. They have a break at lunchtime, when they chat to their friends and in the evenings, if they are free, they probably either watch TV or argue with their families! They are not likely to go out. The weekend begins on
10 Friday, as soon as work, school, or university are over. Many young people go to pubs or discos. They go to bed very late and don't get up the next day until lunchtime. This is repeated on Saturday night. On Saturday afternoon they may go shopping with friends, and on Sunday afternoon they suddenly
15 remember their homework! The summer is the best time of year for young people – students may actually have three free months. Some get part-time jobs to be able to travel, but many just stay at home and enjoy doing nothing, unless they're on holiday with their families. In general, young people today tend
20 to spend their free time together, talking, drinking, and maybe dancing. Probably their parents' generation did the same!

· ·

LISTENING

1 Favourite clothes

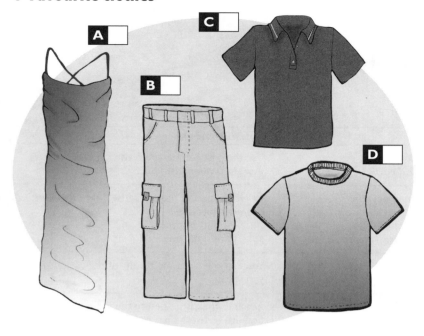

a   **T4.1** Listen to four people talking about their favourite clothes. Match the speakers to the pictures above.

b   Listen again and write the speaker's number in the box. There is one extra sentence you do not need to use.

Who …

a   used to wear formal clothes most of the time?

b   doesn't like spending a lot of money on clothes?

c   needs to buy a new item of clothing?

d   spends a lot of money on clothes?

e   bought their favourite clothes abroad?

2 Is *feng shui* out of control?

a   **T4.2** Listen to a *feng shui* expert. Does she think *feng shui* is out of control? Why (not)?

b   Listen again and decide if the *feng shui* expert thinks the sentences are **T** (true) or **F** (false).

1   If the furniture in your house is in the wrong position, it can make you ill.

2   *Feng shui* is not a religion.

3   Putting a three-legged frog in the right place can make you rich.

4   Not all books about *feng shui* are authentic.

5   *Feng shui* is about using the Earth's natural energy to make your life better.

PRONUNCIATION

1 The /ə/ sound: Sentence rhythm

a   **T4.3** Listen and repeat the /ə/ sound in these words from File 4.

1	fashion**a**ble	6	jeal**ou**s
2	design**e**r	7	cupbo**a**rd
3	**a**rrange	8	furnit**u**re
4	mat**u**re	9	balc**o**ny
5	partn**e**r	10	comfort**a**ble

b   **T4.4** Now listen and repeat six sentences. Focus on pronouncing the /ə/ sound as well as you can.

2  and

T4.5 Write the words. Then listen and repeat them.

1   /skɜːt/   _____

2   /ʃuːz/   _____

3   /ʃɔːtsliːvd/   _____

4   /dɪˈvɔːs/   _____

5   /ʃeə/   _____

6   /ʌnˈsəʊʃəbl/   _____

7   /ˈseksɪst/   _____

8   /ɪmˈpeɪʃnt/   _____

9   /ˈkʊʃən/   _____

10   /ˈstaɪlɪʃ/   _____

Animals or people?

GRAMMAR

1 CHECK WHAT YOU KNOW: The present perfect

a Revise the rules. Then do exercises **b** and **c**.

Present perfect simple

Use	Example	Notes/Problems
For **past experiences** when we don't say when.	*I've been to London.* *Have you ever tried paella?*	Use the past simple when you say when, e.g. *I went to London last year.*
For **unfinished actions** which started in the past and are **still true now**, especially with *be*, *have* (possession), and *know*.	*How long have you known her?* **Since** *1996.* *I've had my car* **for** *two years.* *I haven't smoked* **since** *Tuesday.*	❶ Don't use the present tense. NOT ~~How long do you know her?~~ *since* + point in time *for* + period of time
For **an action in the past** which has **recently finished**.	*We've painted the flat.* *Look. I've done it!*	You can often see the results of the action when you speak.
With *just*, *already*, and *yet*.	*He's just arrived.* *They've already gone.* *The film hasn't started yet.*	*just* and *already* go before the main verb or after *be*, with (+) verbs. *yet* goes at the end of the sentence, in (−) and (?).
With **superlatives**.	*She's the nicest person I've (ever) met.*	(= until now)

b Correct the mistake in each sentence.

1 It's the best book I ever read.

2 I play football since I was a little boy.

3 We are together for six years.

4 I have known her since a long time.

5 You've already have told me.

6 Did he pass his driving test yet?

7 Last month they've driven to Morocco.

8 I don't see you you for ages! How are you?

c Put the verb in brackets in the past simple or present perfect and complete the questions.

1 When _____ he _____ ? (arrive)

2 _____ you _____ yet? (finish)

3 **A** How long _____ _____ _____ here? (live)

   B All my life.

4 What time _____ _____ _____ _____ today? (get up)

5 **A** _____ you ever _____ octopus? (eat)

   B No, I don't like seafood.

6 _____ you _____ the film last night? (see)

7 _____ you _____ Tom Hanks' new film? (see)

8 What's the best novel you _____ ever _____ ? (read)

2 NEW LANGUAGE: Present perfect simple or continuous?

a Underline the correct verb form in these sentences.

1 She's furious with her husband because he's *been crashing/crashed* their new car.

2 He's hot because he's *been running/run* in the park.

3 How long have you *been having/had* your laptop?

4 They've just *bought/been buying* a new semi-detached house.

5 She's already *been making/made* her wedding dress.

6 That was the best documentary I've ever *been seeing/seen*.

7 How many times have you *seen/been seeing* that film?

8 I have *been writing/written* four letters this morning.

9 We've *known/been knowing* them for years.

10 How long have you *waited/been waiting* here?

b Complete the letter with the verbs in the correct form.

Dear Susan,

Sorry I ¹_____ (not write) for ages, but I
²_____ (be) really busy with exams. I
³_____ (finish) now, thank goodness, so I've got a
bit more time to catch up on writing letters.

So, what ⁴_____ (you/do) recently? Apart from
studying, I ⁵_____ (go out) a lot with Mark, do you
remember him? Well, we ⁶_____ (decide) to go on
holiday together, to India for a month. I ⁷_____
(not tell) my family yet, but I'm sure they'll be OK about it.

⁸_____ (you/find) a job yet? I ⁹_____
(look) too, but I ¹⁰_____ (not manage) to find
anything. I still ¹¹_____ (not hear) from an
interview I had last week so I'm keeping my fingers crossed!

Must go. Mark ¹²_____ (just/arrive). Please
write soon.

Love, Julie

VOCABULARY

3 Animals

Name the animals.

1 _____   2 _____   3 _____

 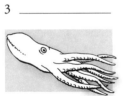 

4 _____   5 _____   6 _____

7 _____   8 _____   9 _____

10 _____ 11 _____ 12 _____

4 Animals and the environment

Write the words for the definitions.

1 a young dog _____
2 an animal with a soft body and no legs
   which is covered by a shell

   _____
3 Some animals, like tigers, are in danger of
   this. _____
4 the act of killing wild animals or birds as
   a sport or to eat _____
5 a group of animals or plants that are all
   the same _____
6 the feet of animals such as dogs, cats and
   bears _____
7 a young cat _____
8 the light, soft things that cover a bird's
   body _____
9 an animal that is kept on farms and used
   for wool or meat _____
10 something an insect or a bird uses for
    flying _____
11 a female bird that is kept for its eggs or its
    meat _____
12 boxes made of wire where an animal is
    kept _____

5 Remember words from the text

Match the sentences. Check you remember
what the **bold** words mean.

1 I think that was a **flash** of lightning. ☐
2 I don't think that skirt is **appropriate**. ☐
3 We **regret** buying our flat. ☐
4 Don't try to **overtake** that car. ☐
5 He's **deaf** and **dumb**. ☐
6 That shop has a **wide variety** of
   clothes. ☐

a He communicates using sign language.
b I think you should get changed into
   something more formal.
c It's going much too fast.
d It's too far from the centre.
e Yes, it looks as if there's a storm coming.
f Whatever style you like, they've got it.

READING AND WRITING

6 Reading

a Quickly read the article. Find two things Jiggs does which are very unusual for a chimpanzee.

Still king of the swingers

Jiggs, the chimpanzee who played Cheetah in 18 Tarzan films with Johnny Weissmuller, has just celebrated his 65th birthday.

Born in Liberia, Jiggs's Hollywood career began in 1933 after he was taken away from his mother in the jungle when he was only a few months old. Tony Gentry, who worked for the the MGM studio, had been sent to Africa to bring back animals for the movies. ¹ ☐

Gentry and Jiggs developed a very strong relationship and Jiggs was quick to respond to human commands and imitate human behaviour – he even learned to write autographs. ² ☐ when they co-starred in Jiggs's debut, *Tarzan and his Mate*.

Johnny Weissmuller adored Jiggs and when the Tarzan actor died in 1984, the chimp joined the funeral procession. However, this has not been the only friend that Jiggs has lost during his lifetime. In 1991, two years

before he died from heart problems, Tony Gentry put him in the care of his nephew, Dan Westfall. 'He had tears in his eyes, when he said, 'I can't take care of Jiggs anymore,' explains Westfall. ³' ☐ '

At 65, Jiggs can still do his favourite acrobatics, although it's more difficult for him now. ⁴' ☐ ' says Westfall. 'He had a painting in the National Gallery in London recently in an exhibition called Ape-stract art.'

Nowadays few fans recognise him on the streets, but people still stop and stare at him. 'After all', says Westfall, ⁵' ☐ '

b Read the text again. Complete with the missing sentences.

> **A** It's unusual to see a chimpanzee riding on the back of a Honda scooter.
> **B** Johnny Weissmuller and Jiggs also became friends instantly
> **C** Jiggs was brought into the States under Gentry's jacket.
> **D** He'd looked after him like a son for more than 50 years.
> **E** He's become a painter since he retired,

c Look at the highlighted words and expressions and guess their meaning from the context. Check with your dictionary.

7 Writing: Organizing ideas

Match the sentences to the paragraphs in the correct order in this **opinion** composition.

> **Should animals be kept in zoos?**
>
> Para 1 (introduction): [c] , ☐ , ☐
> Para 2: ☐ , ☐
> Para 3: ☐ , ☐
> Para 4: ☐ , ☐
> Para 5 (conclusion): ☐ , ☐

. . . .

A Firstly, many zoos are old and dirty and the animals are kept in miserable conditions.

B On the other hand, it is true that a few good zoos play an important role in the conservation of species.

C Man's superiority to animals means that he has always tended to treat them badly.

D However, these are a minority, and in any case this job is better done in protected areas in the countries where the animals live.

E In conclusion, I think that most zoos should be closed down, and animals should only be kept in captivity in conservation areas where they live in their natural environment.

F Many are used to work, others to earn money for him, and others to research consumer products.

G Secondly, the animals often live in a climate which is not natural to them.

H In my opinion, keeping animals in zoos is usually just another example of this cruel treatment.

I Often the cages are so small that the animals suffer psychologically, for example the polar bear, which eventually goes mad in captivity.

J This means that elephants may have to put up with cold and rain, or penguins with heatwaves.

K And if people really want to see animals from far-away countries, they should watch the wildlife documentaries on TV.

. . . .

Can you remember?

> 'There are three things I always forget.
> Names, faces – the third I can't remember.'
> *Italo Svevo, Italian writer*

GRAMMAR

1 CHECK WHAT YOU KNOW: Quantifiers

a Revise the rules. Then do exercises **b** and **c**.

Use	Example	Notes/Problems
Use *both/either/neither* when you talk about two things: 1 use **both** for A and B.	*Both Jim and Jack are coming.* *Both of them are coming.* *They are both coming.*	*both* can go at the beginning of the sentence or before the main verb.
2 use **neither … nor…** for not A and not B.	*Neither Rome nor Madrid has got a port.* *Neither (of them) has got a port.*	*neither* can be used with a sing. or plural verb. The verb must be (+).
3 use **either** for A or B.	*You can have either cake or ice cream.* *You can have either of them.* *Either you or your sister has to go.*	After *either … or* the verb must be singular.
Use **somebody** (or *someone*), **anything**, **anywhere**, etc. when you don't say exactly who/what/where.	*There's something in my eye.* *Can I have something to drink?* *There isn't anything to eat.* *Is anybody* (OR *anyone*) *at home?*	Use *some*(*thing*, etc.) in (+) sentences (and (?) for offers/requests). Use *any*(*thing*, etc.) in (−) sentences and (?). ❶ Don't use a double negative.
Use **nobody** (or *no one*), **nothing**, **nowhere**, etc. to talk about no people or things.	*Nobody came.* *Where did he go? Nowhere.* *There was nothing to do in the town.*	Use *no*(*body*, etc.) in (−) short answers. (= There wasn't anything to do.)

b Complete the text with *both*, *either* or *neither*.

I've got two older sisters, but I don't look like ¹_____ of them. ²_____ of them are extremely tall. In fact, they work as models.

They are ³_____ married, but ⁴_____ of them has children. They are very busy and I haven't seen ⁵_____ of them for over a month.

c Right ☑ or wrong ☒? Correct the wrong sentences.

1 Does somebody know the right answer? ▢

2 I don't know nobody who goes skiing. ▢

3 I'm going to take something for my stomach-ache. ▢

4 We haven't got anything in common. ▢

5 Would you like something to eat? ▢

6 Anyone knows if King Arthur really existed. ▢

7 When you cook the dinner I can never find something afterwards. ▢

8 A Is there anything to eat?
  B No, anything. ▢

2 NEW LANGUAGE: Quantifiers

a Cross out the wrong word.

1 There are *none/no* trees in our street.

2 *All the/All* students in my class are girls.

3 *Most/Most of* people put up with uncomfortable clothes because they want to look fashionable.

4 *All/Everything* has changed in my hometown.

5 I go climbing *all days/every day* in the holidays.

6 *Anybody/Nobody* can wear this dress. You don't have to be a super-model.

7 I've been working hard *all day/every day* and I'm exhausted!

8 *No/None* of my friends are 'new men'.

b Tick ☑ the sentences where you could use *every* instead of *each*.

1 This guest house is great. Each room has its own bathroom and TV. ☐

2 We are very different in my family. Each of us has our own personality. ☐

3 Each customer who buys a new washing machine this week will get a 10% discount. ☐

4 In a football match there are 11 players in each team. ☐

5 The boss decided to talk to each of his employees individually. ☐

6 The language school has given each student a free computer program. ☐

VOCABULARY

3 Use your dictionary: Confused words

Read the dictionary definitions carefully. Then complete the sentences with *memory, souvenir, reminder* or *memorial*.

1 That statue was put up as a _____ to the victims of the bombing.

2 My new computer has a bigger _____ than the old one.

3 We bought a rug as a _____ from our trip to Morocco.

4 My earliest _____ is playing with my rabbit when I was little.

5 I'm going to leave you a note as a _____ that you have to phone the travel agent's.

memory /ˈmeməri/ **noun** (pl *memories*) **1** (C) a person's ability to remember things: *to have a good/bad memory. The drug can affect your short-term memory.* **2** (C, U) the part of your mind in which you store things that you remember: *That day remained firmly in my memory for the rest of my life. Are you going to do your speech from memory, or are you going to use notes?* **3** (C) something that you remember: *That is one of my happiest memories. Childhood memories.* **4** (C, U) the part of a computer where information is stored: *This computer has a 640k memory/640k of memory.*

souvenir /suːvəˈnɪə/ **noun 5** (C) something that you keep to remind you of somewhere you have been on holiday or of a special event: *I brought back a menu as a souvenir of my trip.*

reminder /rɪˈmaɪndə/ **noun** (C) something that makes you remember sth: *We received a reminder from the gas company that we hadn't paid the bill yet.*

memorial /məˈmɔːrɪəl/ **noun** (C) **a memorial to sb/sth** something that is built or done to remind people of an event or person: *a war memorial*

4 Word-building

Complete the text with the correct form of the words in **bold**. Use your dictionary to check.

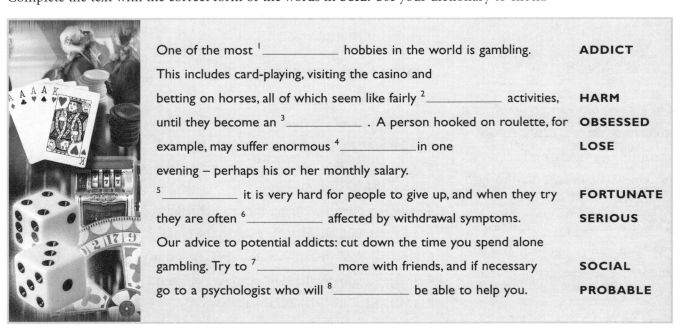

One of the most ¹_____ hobbies in the world is gambling. This includes card-playing, visiting the casino and betting on horses, all of which seem like fairly ²_____ activities, until they become an ³_____ . A person hooked on roulette, for example, may suffer enormous ⁴_____ in one evening – perhaps his or her monthly salary.

⁵_____ it is very hard for people to give up, and when they try they are often ⁶_____ affected by withdrawal symptoms. Our advice to potential addicts: cut down the time you spend alone gambling. Try to ⁷_____ more with friends, and if necessary go to a psychologist who will ⁸_____ be able to help you.

ADDICT

HARM

OBSESSED

LOSE

FORTUNATE

SERIOUS

SOCIAL

PROBABLE

READING AND WRITING

5 Reading

a Read the problems and see if you can work out the answers.

LOGICAL PROBLEMS

1 When Alex, Brian and Chris finished their race they were feeling very tired. It had been raining very heavily, so heavily in fact that the judges couldn't see who came in first, who second, and who third. When they asked the three men, they each made two statements. One man lied in both his statements. The other two told the truth. This is what they said:

Alex said, 'I came in first. Chris was last.'

Brian said, 'Alex wasn't first. Chris came in second.'

Chris said, 'I was before Alex. Brian wasn't second.'

So what was the order in which they crossed the finishing line?

2 I live in a very small village where many people are related to each other. For example Tom, Dick, and Harry are garage owner, vicar and lawyer but not in that order. Tom is the vicar's father-in-law and Dick is the lawyer's son-in-law. Everyone was at church last Saturday when Harry married the garage owner's daughter. **Who does which job?** (By the way, none of the three has been married more than once.)

3 The bus from Edinburgh to London left at 8 a.m. An hour later a cyclist started out from London for Edinburgh. **When the bus and the cyclist meet, which of the two will be further from Edinburgh?**

b Match the answers to the puzzles.

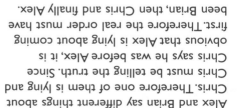

C We know that Tom cannot be the vicar (because he is the vicar's father-in-law), that Dick cannot be the lawyer (he is the son-in-law) and that Harry cannot be the garage owner. We also know that Tom is not the garage owner, Dick is not the vicar, and Harry is not the lawyer ('not in that order'). So Tom must be the lawyer, Dick the garage owner, and Harry the vicar. The vicar is of course already married, but it is one of his jobs to marry other people!

B Alex and Brian say different things about Chris. Therefore one of them is lying and Chris. Therefore one of them is lying and Chris must be telling the truth. Since Chris says he was before Alex, it is obvious that Alex is lying about coming first. Therefore the real order must have been Brian, then Chris and finally Alex.

A The bus and the cyclist are both the same distance from Edinburgh, of course.

6 Writing: Correcting mistakes

Correct the ten typical mistakes in the letter (grammar, vocabulary or spelling).

Dear Caroline,

I'm writting to thank you for your lovely letter. It's ages since we've seen us and it was a lovely surprise to hear from you.

5 The last night I went to that bar where we had our end-of-term drink last year, do you remind? We stayed there until 3 am, dancing and chatting. It was really good fun.

Have you heard from someone else? I'm still in touch with some of our group, like Karen and
10 Christine, but I don't see the others for a long time. Karen has just got married with her boyfriend and Christine is having a baby on June.

That's all for now. Please write me soon. I'm looking forward to hear from you.

15 Love from,

Helen

It's all in the mind

'Coincidence is the window to another world.'
Harry Mulisch, Dutch writer

GRAMMAR

1 CHECK WHAT YOU KNOW: Relative clauses

a Revise the rules. Then do exercise **b**.

Use	Example	Notes/Problems
Use **defining relative clauses** to give essential information about a person, place or thing.	*She's the woman who/that works with me.* *It's a shop which/that sells candles.* *It's a place where you can do sport.* *He's the boy whose father owns the school.* *She's the girl (who) I met last summer.*	Use *who* for people, *which* for animals/things, and *where* for places. You can also use *that* instead of *who/which*. *whose* = of who/which *who* and *which* are often omitted when the verb after the relative pronoun has a different subject.
Use **non-defining relative clauses** to give extra information about a person, place or thing.	*My grandmother, who's nearly 80, still cooks every day.* *This book, which was published last year, has sold 100,000 copies.*	Always put commas (or a comma and a full stop) before and after the clause. ❶ You can't use *that* instead of *who/which*. NOT ~~This book, that was sold last year…~~ You can't omit the relative pronoun here.

b Correct the sentences.

1 Mrs Brown, that has lived next door to me all my life, is a faith-healer.

2 The presenter who his son is a mountaineer retired last year.

3 That's the laboratory where Tom works there.

4 My mother gave me the chest of drawers what is in your bedroom.

5 The story I read it in the newspaper yesterday turned out not to be true.

6 Many animals who live in zoos are endangered species.

7 His operation, that lasted four hours, was completely successful.

8 My boss, whose always pulling my leg, is a really funny person.

2 NEW LANGUAGE: Relative clauses with prepositions

Rewrite the first part of the sentences to make them informal. Leave out the relative pronoun where you can.

EXAMPLE
The safari on which I went was thrilling.
The safari I went on was thrilling.

1 **The man to whom those puppies belong** has promised to give me one.

_____

2 **The flat into which they moved** had been unoccupied for years.

_____

3 **The organization for which my sister works** meets every Monday.

_____

4 **One of the women with whom I work** has just bought a terraced house.

_____

5 **His wife, in whom he had trusted completely**, betrayed him to the police.

b Complete the sentences with *what*, *which* or *whom*.

¹_____ I really wanted was a relaxing holiday, so I decided on a week in the Caribbean. The travel agent with ²_____ I booked promised that the trip would be wonderful. However he did not give me my ticket straight away, ³_____ surprised me. Then when I finally received it I saw that the plane in ⁴_____ I would be travelling was a charter flight, not the scheduled flight I'd been promised. I began to get suspicious. When I arrived at the airport on the day of the trip, the tour representative told me that my name wasn't on his list. At first I couldn't believe ⁵_____ he was saying, but when I finally realised that it was true, I got really angry. In the end he managed to find me another holiday, for ⁶_____ I had to pay extra. When I got there the people with ⁷_____ I was sharing the apartment turned out to be very nice, and the beach was wonderful, ⁸_____ was a relief. However, ⁹_____ I would like to know is whether the travel agent actually knew he had overbooked the trip or if it was just a genuine mistake.

VOCABULARY

3 Supernatural vocabulary

Write the missing consonants.

1 a feeling that something unpleasant is going to happen in the future __ __e__o__i__io__

2 when two or more things happen together at the same time, by chance __oi__ __i__e__ __e

3 the spirit of a dead person seen or heard by people still living __ __o__ __

4 the part of a person that some people think still exists after they die __ou__

5 a person who has special powers to see into the future __ __ai__ __o__a__ __

6 the communication of thoughts between the minds of two people without using speech, signs or writing __e__e__a__ __y

7 adjective (informal) to describe sth frightening and possibly supernatural __ __oo__y

4 Use your dictionary: Words with more than one meaning

a Decide which is the correct meaning of *miss* in each sentence. Write the number in the box.

> **miss** /mɪs/ **verb 1** (I, T) to fail to hit or catch something **2** (T) to not see, hear, understand, sb/sth **3** (T) to arrive too late for sth **4** (T) to feel sad because sb or sth is not with you any more **5** (T) to notice that sb/sth is not where he/she/it should be **6** (T) to avoid sth unpleasant

1 I didn't hear my alarm this morning so I missed my bus. ☐ 3

2 We would have won the match if he hadn't missed the penalty. ☐

3 I'm going to leave early in order to miss the rush-hour traffic. ☐

4 I didn't miss my purse until it was too late. ☐

5 When my partner goes away on business I miss him terribly. ☐

6 I missed the end of the film because my grandparents phoned. ☐

b Read the definitions and try to think of one word with both meanings. Check with your dictionary.

1 _____
   a things that you drink out of
   b things you use to see better

2 _____
   a do a picture of something with a pencil or pen
   b the result of a game in which both teams get the same points

3 _____
   a light in colour (esp. for hair)
   b right, just, treating each side equally

4 _____
   a well, in good health or happy
   b money you pay for breaking the law

5 _____
   a a formal set of clothes consisting of a jacket and either a skirt or trousers
   b make you look attractive

6 _____
   a show where something is by using your finger
   b a particular fact, idea or opinion that sb expresses

7 _____
   a a young cow
   b the back of your leg below the knee

READING AND WRITING

5 Reading

Premonitions
– A vision of the future?

PREMONITIONS of danger, death, and disaster are the most common kind of psychic experience. Several scientific studies of premonitions show not only that premonitions really do happen but that they are common. An American survey of high school students found that one out of twelve had experienced psychic dreams – about half of them premonitions of future events. A similar survey of adults showed that 30% of people interviewed experienced psychic dreams. 90% of them were female, and most of the premonitions were about persons and events in the dreamers' own lives.

An English psychologist Dr. Keith Hearne did a study of 127 people who had experienced premonitions. Hearne gave them psychological tests and found that they were more emotional than the average person but in other respects were normal. He was able to document several remarkable premonitions of disasters. Although the majority of premonitions came in dreams, some came when the person was awake. For example, on June 1, 1974, an American woman, Lesley Brennan, was watching TV at midday when she saw the words 'News Flash' appear on the screen. A man's voice said that there had been an explosion at a chemical plant in the nearby town of Flixborough. Several people had been killed and many injured. Lesley mentioned the news to a couple who were staying with her at the house. That evening they all watched the news from Flixborough of the Nypro chemical plant explosion that killed 28 people and injured hundreds more, but they could not understand why the newsreader said that the explosion had happened late in the afternoon – at 4.53 p.m. Later they realized that Brennan had experienced a premonition of the massive explosion – five hours before it actually happened.

a Read the text and mark the sentences **T** (true) or **F** (false).

1 According to scientific research, premonitions are not unusual. ☐

2 One out of twelve high school students in the survey had had a premonition in a dream. ☐

3 Adult women experience more premonitions than anybody else. ☐

4 People who have premonitions are no different from anyone else. ☐

5 People usually have premonitions when they are asleep. ☐

6 Lesley Brennan dreamt that she saw a news flash about an accident. ☐

7 Lesley and her visitors were surprised when they saw the evening news. ☐

b Look at the highlighted words/expressions and guess their meaning. How are they pronounced? Check with your dictionary.

6 Writing: Using relative clauses

Complete the narrative composition with the correct relative clause A–J.

A who was wearing a dirty old dressing-gown

B who had opened the door for us

C where we would be able to spend a quiet fortnight alone

D which was so hot we couldn't bear it

E we had seen the night before

F which the travel agent had given us

G which is why nobody could open it

H whose eyes seemed to be full of tears

I which was full of old and dusty furniture, and had no TV

J which we had shut before going to bed

Describe a frightening experience you have had

We had such a fright last summer when we arrived at our holiday destination. We had imagined a country cottage in a picturesque village, ¹☐ . However, when we arrived at the address ²☐ we could not believe our eyes. The house was opened by a thin old lady, ³☐ . She showed us into the living room, ⁴☐ , and then left us without saying anything. As it was late we went up to the bedroom, ⁵☐ . We tried to open the windows but they were tightly shut, so we got into the bed, and tried to get to sleep. After a short time we heard a noise and we looked up and saw a young man, ⁶☐ , trying desperately to open the window just as we had done. When he saw us, he disappeared through the door, ⁷☐ . Our immediate reaction was to jump out of bed, grab our things and spend the night in the car. The next day we discovered that the man ⁸☐ had commited suicide by jumping out of the window in our bedroom forty years before. Every year since then, on the anniversary of his death, he had been seen in the room trying to open this window. Since then, however, his wife, the woman ⁹☐ , had kept the window locked, ¹⁰☐ .

LISTENING

1 Saved by a gorilla

a T5.1 Listen to the news report about a female gorilla called Binti. What did she do?

b Listen again and answer the questions.

1 Where did the incident take place?

_____

_____

2 How old was:

  a the boy? _____   c Binti's child? _____

  b Binti? _____

3 How far did the boy fall?

_____

4 Where did he land?

_____

5 What did Binti do?

_____

6 Why had the zookeepers given Binti dolls to play with?

_____

2 It's a small world!

BREAKFASTS

a T5.2 Listen to four people talking about coincidences they have had. What do all the stories have in common?

b Listen again and match a sentence to each speaker. There is one extra sentence.

Who …

a met a relative who they hadn't seen for a long time? ☐

b met someone they had been trying to contact? ☐

c couldn't escape from a person they didn't want to be with? ☐

d had a premonition of the person they were going to meet? ☐

e met an ex-colleague of their partner's? ☐

PRONUNCIATION

1 Sentence rhythm

T5.3 Listen and repeat six sentences. Try to copy the rhythm.

2 Multi-syllable words

a Underline the stressed syllable in these words.

1 environment	7 chimpanzee
2 telepathy	8 premonition
3 coincidence	9 illegal
4 species	10 clairvoyant
5 volunteer	11 research
6 memorize	12 wildlife

b T5.4 Repeat the words after the cassette.

3 Silent letters

a Look at the phonetics and definitions and write the words. Be careful! They all have a silent consonant.

1 _____ /ˈsaɪəns/ the study of the physical world

2 _____ /ˈsuːdənɪm/ a name used, e.g. by a writer instead of his/her real name

3 _____ /læm/ a young sheep

4 _____ /ˈfɒrən/ not from your country

5 _____ /nɒk/ make a noise by hitting sth with your hand, e.g. a door

6 _____ /ˈwɪsəl/ make a noise by blowing air between your lips

7 _____ /ˈaɪən/ a hard strong metal

8 _____ /kɑːm/ relaxed, not stressed or nervous

9 _____ /ˈfæsɪneɪtɪd/ very interested

10 _____ /ˈɑːnsə/ say sth in response to a question

b T5.5 Listen and practise saying the words.

Caught in the act

'Behind every great fortune there is a crime.'
Honoré de Balzac, French writer

GRAMMAR

1 CHECK WHAT YOU KNOW: Gerund (verb + -*ing*), infinitive (with/without *to*)

a Revise the rules. Then do exercises **b** and **c**.

Use	Example	Notes/Problems
Use **the gerund:** 1 after **prepositions** 2 after **certain verbs** 3 as the **subject of a sentence** 4 after **certain expressions**	*She left without saying goodbye.* *I love cooking but I hate washing up.* *Eating in restaurants is expensive.* *This film's not worth seeing – it's awful.*	See Student's Book, **ex. 2**, *p.86* for a list of verbs.
Use *to* + **infinitive:** 1 after **certain verbs** 2 after **adjectives** 3 after **question words**	*Would you like to come?* *I'm hoping to get a better job soon.* *It's difficult to learn a language.* *I didn't know what to do.*	See Student's Book, **ex. 2**, *p.86* for a list of verbs.
Use **infinitive** (without *to*): 1 after **most modal and auxiliary verbs.** 2 after *make* and *let.* 3 after **some expressions** (*would rather, had better*, etc.).	*Did you like it?* *You shouldn't go.* *My mother won't let me go.* *They made me work hard.* *I'd rather be at home.* *You'd better hurry.*	*ought to, have to*, and *used to* are exceptions. When *make* is used in the passive it's followed by *to* + infinitive, e.g. *I was made to work hard.* (= I'd prefer to be at home.) (= You really should hurry.)

b Complete the sentences with a verb from the list in the correct form.

arrive   attack   escape   go   have   live   make   not tell   stop   work out

1 Laura didn't enjoy _____ the massage.

2 The lion managed _____ from the zoo.

3 The new presenter of the show is so bad it's made me _____ watching it.

4 Do you fancy _____ out tonight?

5 I'd rather _____ in the country than in the city.

6 Do you think you'll be able _____ the answer?

7 It's a secret. I've promised _____ anyone.

8 You must _____ on time for the interview.

9 Sharks avoid _____ dolphins as they know they might get hurt.

10 My boss doesn't let me _____ personal phone calls at work.

c Right ✓ or wrong ✗? Correct the wrong sentences.

1 Smoke is prohibited here.   ☐

2 She accused me of looking down on her.   ☐

3 I don't know where get off the bus.   ☐

4 We'd better go. It's late.   ☐

5 It's never easy to accept that a relationship is over.   ☐

6 I couldn't decide which hat to buy.   ☐

7 It's not worth to go to a clairvoyant.   ☐

8 The burglar got in without make a noise.   ☐

9 I'm looking forward to see you.   ☐

10 It took me ages to get used to drive on the left.   ☐

2 NEW LANGUAGE: Verb + infinitive or gerund?

Underline the correct alternative in each sentence.

1 Alan forgot *to find out/finding out* what time the film started.

2 Your car needs *to clean/cleaning*.

3 I'm trying *to find/finding* a pair of purple boots.

4 Remember *to empty/emptying* the rubbish bin.

5 The climbers needed *to rest/resting* several times.

6 I definitely remember *to save/saving* that document, but now I can't find it anywhere.

7 If it doesn't work the first time, try *to insert/inserting* the floppy disc again.

8 I'll never forget *to see/seeing* Venice for the first time. It was a pity that I'd forgotten *to take/taking* my camera.

VOCABULARY

3 Crime vocabulary

Complete the crossword.

Across

2 Another expression for the death penalty is _____ punishment.

5 a sum of money that you have to pay for breaking the law

7 a person who steals something from a shop

8 the process in a court of law where a person is found guilty or not guilty

13 the facts, signs, etc. that make you believe something is true

14 when the police take someone prisoner in order to question them about a crime

Down

1 an official who acts as a judge in cases involving less serious crimes

3 a crime or an illegal action

4 the decision which states that a person is guilty or innocent

6 a person who steals purses and wallets from other people in public places

9 a person who sees something happen and can tell other people about it later

10 the general word for a person who steals something from another person

11 take something from someone without permission and with no intention of returning it

12 the group of people who listen to the facts in a court case and decide if the person is guilty or innocent

4 Collocation

Match the verbs and expressions.

accuse   arrest   be released
be tried   break   commit   find
have   rob   steal

1 _____ a crime

2 _____ the law

3 _____ a bank

4 _____ money from a bank

5 _____ a clue

6 _____ a suspected person

7 _____ him/her of the crime

8 _____ in court

9 _____ an alibi

10 _____ from custody

5 Pronunciation

Match words with the same pronunciation.

throw   **daugh**ter   qu**eue**
suffer   **coffee**

1 b**ough**t   _____

2 en**ough**   _____

3 c**ough**   _____

4 alth**ough**   _____

5 thr**ough**   _____

READING AND WRITING

6 Reading

a Read the article and find out where the pickpocket usually worked and why he was caught this time. As you read, try to guess the missing words but don't write them.

Pickpocket chooses the wrong victim

A ⟨1⟩ from France, who was trying to rob members of the US Athletics team, was lying in a Spanish ⟨2⟩ yesterday after being chased and captured by the sprinter Maurice Greene, currently the fastest man on Earth. Greene and his team mates were in Seville, southern Spain, for the World Athletics Championships.

Greene, who broke the 100-metre world record in Athens, ran after the thief at the airport in Seville, after seeing him put his ⟨3⟩ into the bag of another member of the American team.

It took Greene, who is capable of covering 100 metres in only 9.79 seconds, just a few seconds to ⟨4⟩ the pickpocket as he tried to run away across the airport. Greene, with the help of Larry Wade, a 110 metre hurdler, held the thief against a wall until Spanish police arrived at the scene. They immediately ⟨5⟩ the surprised pickpocket although he tried to pretend he was an ⟨6⟩ French tourist. He was, however, unable to explain why he had started to run across the airport ⟨7⟩.

Police said yesterday that he was a ⟨8⟩ pickpocket with an extensive police record whose speciality was to travel to major international events that attracted large ⟨9⟩ of visitors. They added that he had already been detained on 24 separate occasions and was going to be ⟨10⟩ from Spain.

b Read the article again. Number the words below 1–10.

innocent	☐	hand	☐
crowds	☐	police cell	☐
professional	☐	expelled	☐
catch	☐	arrested	☐
pickpocket	☐	lounge	☐

7 Writing: Punctuation

Punctuate this letter to a newspaper to complain about the increase in street crime.

dear sir/madam.

i am writing to express my concern about the increase in street crime in my area central london

on 22nd september last year i was walking along baker street one evening when I was robbed by two young men wearing leather jackets and carrying knives when i shouted help me the only person who was in the street a man of about 40 did nothing and just walked away

i would like to suggest to the public in general that if we do not help each other and stand up to criminals like these none of us will be safe as for the man who refused to help me i would like to ask him one question would you like to be mugged and have your weeks money stolen from you

thank you for your attention

yours faithfully

mr r m cole

Economical with the truth

GRAMMAR

1 CHECK WHAT YOU KNOW: Reported speech

a Revise the rules. Then do exercise **b**.

Use	Example	Notes/Problems
Use **reported speech** to talk or write in the past about what somebody said or asked.	*I asked him where he lived.* *He said (that) he lived in Milan.* *She told me she was coming.* *He said he might stay.* *They told us they were coming the next day.*	In reported speech, the verb tense changes (present → past, past/present perfect → past perfect, *will* → *would*, etc.) Most modal verbs stay the same. Certain time expressions change, e.g. *today* → *that day*, *last night* → *the night before*, etc.
Use **reported statements** for what somebody said.	*He said (that) he lived alone.* *She told me (that) she hadn't finished.*	Use *said* or *told* + person. NOT ~~She said me…~~ *that* after *said/told me* is optional.
Use **reported questions** for what somebody asked.	*He asked me what my name was.* *He asked me if/whether I liked sport.*	The word order is subject + verb. NOT ~~He asked me what was my name., She asked me did I like sport.~~
Use **reported imperatives** to talk about what somebody told you or asked you to do.	*He told us to come.* *She told them not to wait.* *We asked him to tell us the time.*	NOT ~~He told us that we came.~~ The negative infinitive is *not to* (+ verb). For requests use *asked* not *told*.

b Write the conversation in reported speech.

1 'What time did you get home last night?'

 Doreen asked Jim _____ .

2 'I arrived just before midnight.'

 Jim replied _____ .

3 'So where were you from eight o'clock until midnight?'

 Doreen asked _____ .

4 'I was working late.'

 He replied _____ .

5 'You've worked late every night this week.'

 Doreen said _____ .

6 'We have to finish the project by the end of the month.'

 Jim told her _____ .

7 'When will we have some time together?'

 Doreen asked him _____ .

8 'Can you turn on the TV, please?'

 Jim asked _____ .

9 'Don't be so lazy!'

 Doreen told him _____ .

2 NEW LANGUAGE: Other reporting verbs

a Correct these typical mistakes.

1 My teacher advised me that I took the exam.

2 James offered giving me a lift home.

3 He apologized for break the vase.

4 She asked me that I didn't tell anybody.

5 The blackmailer threatened selling the photos.

6 They agreed changing my jacket for a bigger size.

b Rewrite the sentences using the verb in brackets.

1 'Yes, it was me. I killed him.' (admit)

 The murderer _____ .

2 'Remember, don't be biased.' (remind the jury)

 The judge _____ .

3 'I didn't steal the money.' (deny)

 The burglar _____ .

4 'Let's go on a safari together.' (persuade us)

 Our friends _____ .

5 'I think you should take a taxi.' (recommend)

 My friend _____ .

6 'I wish I'd studied more when I was younger.' (regret)

 My sister _____ .

VOCABULARY

3 Lying vocabulary

Complete the sentences with a word from the list.

catch	cheat	deceive	keep	lies	pretend	truth	white lie

1 My friends are very discreet. They always _____ my secrets.

2 'Are you telling me the _____ about what happened?'

3 'It's not true. You've been trying to _____ me!'

4 If you tell _____ you'll get caught.

5 I hate people who _____ at cards.

6 When she asked me if I thought she was beautiful, I told a _____ and said yes.

7 Children often _____ to be asleep so they don't have to get up in the morning.

8 Someone will always _____ you out if you tell lies.

4 Reporting verbs

Underline the verb that makes more sense.

1 The doctor *warned/advised* me that it was dangerous for me to fly.

2 The burglar *threatened/promised* to hurt us if we made a noise.

3 My husband *reminded/encouraged* me to learn to play golf.

4 He *admitted/denied* taking the money and offered to pay it back.

5 We didn't know what to do, so my partner *suggested/regretted* going to the cinema.

6 She *agreed/refused* to tidy her room although I asked her six times.

7 He *apologized for/recommended* not phoning, and explained that he'd been away.

8 My father *admitted/insisted* on watching the football, though we all wanted to see a film.

5 Use your dictionary: Finding the right word

a Look at the dictionary extract to see how it gives several word forms.

> **choose** /tʃuːz/ verb (pt **chose** pp **chosen**) to decide which thing or person you want out of the ones which are available » noun **choice**

b Use your dictionary to find the following words. The headword for each is the **bold** word.

1 an adjective for a person who always tells the **truth**

_____

2 the adjective for a person who likes to keep things **secret**

_____

3 an idiom with **clue** meaning to know nothing about sth

_____

4 an adjective from **pretend** to describe a person who tries to appear more serious or important than he/she really is

_____

5 a phrasal verb with **cheat** meaning to be unfaithful to sb

_____

6 Pronunciation: /ð/ and /θ/

Put the words into the correct column.

breath   breathe   faithful   neither   rather sunbathe   telepathy   thief   those   though thought   threaten   truth   worth

ð	θ

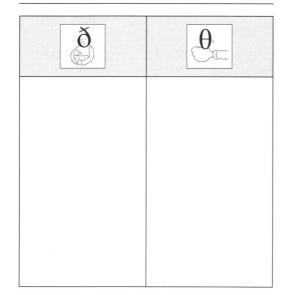

READING AND WRITING

7 Reading

a Quickly read the text, and match the topic sentences (A–D) to the correct paragraph (1–4).

A The hunt for Butch and Sundance was one of the Pinkertons' most famous investigations.

B The archives of the Pinkerton detectives, America's first and greatest criminal investigators, have been donated to the Library of Congress.

C But despite being their most famous hunt, it was also one of their least successful.

D The agency was founded in 1850 by Allan Pinkerton, a Scottish immigrant who left Glasgow to avoid arrest as a radical.

Pinkerton Papers tell the story of justice in the Wild West

1 ☐ The ninety boxes of material cover the period from 1853 to 1937, recording some of the most celebrated cases in US criminal history, such as the search for Butch Cassidy and the Sundance Kid.

2 ☐ It was the first agency to carry out private detective work and its organisational structure later provided the model for the FBI. The Pinkerton logo, a single staring eye above the words 'The eye that never sleeps' was the origin of the expression 'private eye' (meaning a private detective).

3 ☐ Butch, a soft-spoken Mormon whose real name was Robert Leroy Parker, escaped to South America with Sundance (Harry Longabaugh) and his mistress Etta Place after robbing a large number of banks and trains without the violence normally associated with this type of crime.

4 ☐ Pinkerton's never caught up with them. The archives contain a wanted poster in Spanish looking for information on the criminals and an account by Frank Dimaio, a Pinkerton detective, describing his search through Argentina for them. According to the agency archives Butch and Sundance were shot dead by Bolivian troops in 1911, a theory supported by forensic evidence.

b Read the article again carefully and answer the questions.

1 Who now has all the papers and other material from Pinkerton's agency?

_____

2 What modern organization was inspired by Pinkerton's?

_____

3 Where does the expression 'private eye' come from?

_____

4 In what way were Butch and Sundance unusual criminals?

_____

5 What shows that it is very likely that they were killed by Bolivian soldiers?

_____

c Underline any new words/expressions and try to guess their meaning from context. Then check with your dictionary.

8 Writing: Using more precise vocabulary

Improve the composition by replacing the phrases *in italics* with a more precise reporting verb. Make any other necessary changes.

· ·

A disastrous party

Last week Mike [1] *asked me if I wanted to go* invited me to go to a party. Although I don't usually like parties, [2] *I said I would go*, as I hadn't been to one for ages.

But when the day of the party came, I had **completely** forgotten about it. At 8.30 Mike phoned me [3] *to tell me to remember* to bring a bottle of wine, and I suddenly remembered the invitation. At that moment I was **watching** TV, and I really didn't feel like going out, but I had [4] *said I definitely would go*, so in the end I quickly got changed.

On the way there Mike [5] *told me to be careful* not to talk about politics, as the Prime Minister's son was going to be there. But as soon as we arrived I forgot, and started talking about TV and [6] *telling everyone that they ought to watch* this new TV show which criticized the government. I then realized what I was saying, and in my embarrassment I spilt my glass of wine on the carpet. I [7] *said I was sorry* to the hosts, and, feeling awful, asked Mike to take me home. But he [8] *told me that he really wanted me to stay*, so I did, drinking more than I should have and not really enjoying myself.

Of course, the next day I had a terrible hangover.

· ·

Secret stories

GRAMMAR

1 NEW LANGUAGE: Connectors

a Cross out the incorrect word.

1 *Although/However* there were several witnesses, they couldn't identify the burglar.

2 The traffic in the city centre has improved a lot. *Though/On the other hand* there is still a lot of vandalism.

3 I'm much better now at using the new software. *However/Also,* I still often have to look at the manual.

4 I definitely recommend visiting Barcelona. The city itself is wonderful, and you can *also/as well* easily get to the beach.

5 I passed the exam *even though/on the other hand* I had missed a lot of classes.

b Complete the text with a suitable connector from the list. One connector can be used more than once.

although   in spite of   so as not to   to
because   because of   so that   for

c Rewrite the sentences using the words in brackets.

1 Tina told a white lie because she didn't want to offend her friend. (so as)

_____

2 He'd been smoking for years, but he didn't find it hard to give up. (even though)

_____

3 Our flight was delayed. There'd been a terrible storm. (because of)

_____

4 The jokes were awful, but everybody enjoyed his speech. (despite)

_____

5 I switched on the computer because I wanted to check my e-mail. (to)

_____

6 He pretended to recognize her, in spite of not being able to remember who she was. (although)

_____

7 I gave my daughter some money. She wanted to buy a Barbie doll. (so that)

_____

8 The reviews were very bad, but the film was still a box-office success. (in spite of)

_____

DESIGNER KIDS

When Mr R J Collins was asked why he had stolen six pairs of designer trainers of different sizes from a shoe shop in Bath, Avon, he replied, '1_____ my children do not feel discriminated against when they go to school.' This highlights a problem many parents have today 2_____ the price of designer label clothes and the desire of their children to wear them.

We asked a number of teenagers why they wore this type of clothing and they came out with a variety of reasons. Many said, '3_____ look different from everybody else,' some said, '4_____ they're the most comfortable clothes around,' and one teenager even said, '5_____ make a good impression on the opposite sex.'

The most surprising thing in the boom of designer clothes is that so many parents can afford to buy them 6_____ the price. 7_____ younger children only used to want to be given toys, they are now asking for designer sportswear 8_____ birthdays or Christmas, and teenagers save up their pocket money for ages just 9_____ buy an Armani shirt or a pair of Nike trainers.

VOCABULARY

2 Revision: Money

a Complete with verbs connected with money.

1 **o**＿＿＿＿ money to someone you've borrowed from

2 **i**＿＿＿＿ money from a relative who has died

3 **g**＿＿＿ **a**＿＿＿＿ money to charity

4 **i**＿＿＿＿ money in stocks and shares

5 **w**＿＿＿＿ money on things you don't need

6 **s**＿＿＿＿ money by putting a little in the bank every week

b Label the pictures.

1 ＿＿＿＿＿＿ 2 ＿＿＿＿＿＿ 3 ＿＿＿＿＿＿

4 ＿＿＿＿＿＿ 5 ＿＿＿＿＿＿ 6 ＿＿＿＿＿＿

3 Business verbs

Choose a, b, or c for each sentence.

1 Jack decided to ＿＿＿ his own business a few years ago.

  a set up b put up c take over

2 He bought a factory to ＿＿＿ mobile telephones.

  a manufacture b market c expand

3 At first the business ＿＿＿ a loss.

  a was having b was making c was doing

4 But after six months the business took off and Jack ＿＿＿ more successful.

  a had b went c became

5 Now he is the ＿＿＿ in the production of mobile phones.

  a market leader b manufacturer c company

6 He has ＿＿＿ many of the smaller mobile phone companies.

  a made up b taken over c set up

7 Next year he is going to start ＿＿＿ to other countries in the EU.

  a exporting b expanding c manufacturing

8 His brother tried to start a similar business but he ran out of money and went ＿＿＿ .

  a bankrupt b in debt c a profit

4 Compound nouns

Write one word in each space to form three compound nouns.

1 ＿＿＿＿ manufacturer / park / thief

2 letter / toy / phone ＿＿＿＿

3 ＿＿＿＿ school / licence / test

4 stage / brand / first ＿＿＿＿

5 ＿＿＿＿ deal / partner / studies

6 passport / quality / air traffic ＿＿＿＿

7 ＿＿＿＿ manager / loan / account

8 detective / love / fairy ＿＿＿＿

5 Remember phrasal verbs

Complete the phrasal verbs with the missing particles.

1 Although I cheated in the exam, I got ＿＿＿ ＿＿＿ it because the teacher didn't see me.

2 When the princess kissed the frog, it turned ＿＿＿ a prince!

3 Don't forget to pick ＿＿＿ the children from school this afternoon.

4 My daughter's very good at making ＿＿＿ stories. Maybe when she grows ＿＿＿ she'll be a novelist!

5 I was really embarassed when I was caught ＿＿＿ lying by the police. I said I'd been driving slowly, but their radar said it was 150kph.

READING AND WRITING

6 Reading

a Read the article quickly to find out how Barbie has changed over the years. Don't worry about the gaps.

If little girls could vote …

In 1959 in California a little but curiously well-developed little girl entered American life for the first time. Since then she has had a number of careers, among them model, astronaut, rap musician, Unicef ambassador, Marine corps sergeant, paediatrician, air hostess, firefighter, and skater. ¹☐ Has the world gone mad?

Love her or hate her, she has become established in the world as part of the American culture, along with Coca Cola, the hamburger and the cigarette. ²☐ and 150 new models are produced every year. Ninety-five per cent of American girls have a Barbie, with the average child possessing ten. The doll is the brand leader in 150 countries worldwide; two are sold every second.

For the first forty years of her life, Barbie looked like the perfect woman until Mattel, her maker, decided to move with the times and get rid of her excessively feminine image. In 1998 Barbie was given a smaller bust, thicker waist and more proportionate hips which meant that she lost her impossible body shape. ³☐

The first Barbie to appear with this new look was 'Really Rad(ical) Barbie' and a number of new friends have also been introduced to emphasize the new era of political correctness. The first was 'Share-a-smile Becky', a blonde doll in a hot pink wheelchair, who wears a disability rights T-shirt. ⁴☐ These were soon followed by three new ethnic companions for Christie, Barbie's previous black friend.

b Match the sentences (A–D) with the gaps (1–4) in the text.

> **A** She was joined by 'Sign Language Barbie', who has one hand showing the sign for 'I love you'.
>
> **B** Now she wears less make-up, has a smaller mouth and avoids the colour pink.
>
> **C** More than a billion Barbie dolls have been sold worldwide
>
> **D** Recently a new 'presidential' model has been released complete with its own podium.

c Read the article again carefully. How do you think the title should finish?

7 Use your dictionary: Checking pronunciation

a Use your instinct to underline the stressed syllable in these words from the text.

1 developed	5 proportionate	8 wheelchair
2 ambassador	6 emphasize	9 disability
3 paediatrician	7 correctness	10 ethnic
4 average		

b Check with your dictionary.

8 Writing: Correcting mistakes

The person who wrote this e-mail typed so quickly that she made ten mistakes. Underline and correct them.

> Hi Angela,
>
> I been away in holiday so I've only just read your e-mail. Great news about the new work ! It sounds much more better than the old one. When do you start? Have you to sell your house and buy a new one, or will you just rent a flat for the moment? Don't forget sending me your new adress and phone number.
>
> Here nothing has changed – in fact I'm getting a bit tired of trying to cope whit work and the family! Still, I suppose no news are better than bad news! Please keep on touch. I promise to answer! Love, Kate

LISTENING

1 Criminal or victim?

a **T6.1** Listen to Julia talking about an unpleasant experience. What was she accused of? Was she guilty?

b Listen again and mark the sentences **T** (true) or **F** (false).

1　She was going to Paris for a holiday. ☐
2　She had something to eat before going to the bookshop. ☐
3　She is keen on looking around bookshops. ☐
4　It was a small bookshop. ☐
5　She changed her mind about buying a book. ☐
6　She put the book back where she found it. ☐
7　When the woman stopped her there wasn't anybody else in the street. ☐
8　The woman had seen Julia putting a book in her bag. ☐
9　The woman didn't say sorry. ☐
10　Julia went to complain to the manager. ☐

2 Old favourites

a **T6.2** Listen to four people talking about their favourite toys. Match the speakers 1–4 to four of the toys below.

b Listen again and match the sentences to the speakers. Who …

a　played with their toy with a brother or sister? ☐ ☐
b　keeps their toy in their bedroom? ☐
c　has a toy which is partly broken now? ☐
d　was given their toy to cheer them up? ☐
e　played with a toy that wasn't really his/hers? ☐
f　has a toy that's over 50? ☐
h　learnt something useful from playing with their toy? ☐

PRONUNCIATION

1 ough/aught; /t/, /θ/, /ð/ and /d/

a **T6.3** Listen and repeat the sentences. See Tapescript on *p.79* if necessary.

2 Word stress

a **T6.4** Listen and repeat the words. Underline the stress.

1　car theft
2　drug dealing
3　a safari park
4　a dressing-gown
5　an office job
6　a guinea pig
7　a life sentence
8　a tracksuit
9　an e-mail
10　a dishwasher
11　a fireplace
12　a health centre

b **T6.5** Listen and answer the questions with a word or phrase from **a** above. Try to get the stress right.

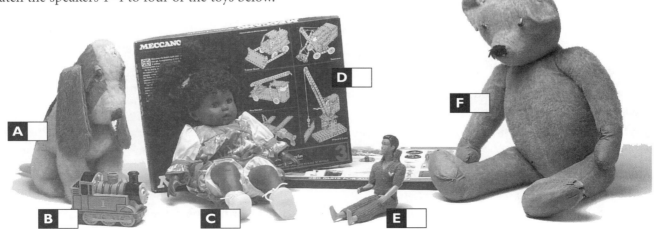

A ☐　B ☐　C ☐　D ☐　E ☐　F ☐

If you can smell it, you can sell it

Smell is breath's brother.
Patrick Susskind, author of the novel 'Perfume'

GRAMMAR

1 NEW LANGUAGE: *as* or *like*?

a Right ☑ or wrong ☒? Correct the wrong sentences.

1 My cousin works like an executive in a multinational company. ☐

2 We used our towels as blankets because we were so cold at night. ☐

3 Some people, as psychologists, are good at spotting liars. ☐

4 My brother looks as my mother, tall and slim. ☐

5 I didn't hear my alarm clock, so I missed the bus like usual. ☐

6 He lives like a king because his mother does everything for him. ☐

7 As you know, I really don't agree with the new marketing plan. ☐

8 He behaves as the boss, but really he's just one of the staff. ☐

9 The company made a loss again, just like last year. ☐

10 The advertising campaign was a great success, as we expected. ☐

b Complete with *as* or *like*.

1 The actress uses her mother's name _____ her stage name.

2 My sister was _____ a mother to me when I was little.

3 The tune of their new single is just _____ their last one.

4 That journalist has worked _____ a foreign correspondent in the Balkans.

5 Some people use low blood pressure _____ an excuse not to go to work.

6 He's very well-built. He looks _____ a rugby player.

7 _____ I was saying before the break, this is an important point.

8 This room is _____ a sauna. Open the window.

2 Verbs of the senses

Complete with a verb of the senses + *like* or *as if* where necessary.

1 Some people think that Oasis _sound like_ the Beatles.

2 Naomi Campbell _____ her mother.

3 I love wearing silk pyjamas. They make me _____ I was a millionaire.

4 Try some of this curry. It _____ delicious.

5 I'm not going to drink this milk. It _____ it's gone off.

6 Your head _____ very hot. I think you've got a temperature.

7 I don't think Nescafé _____ real coffee.

8 You're very white. You _____ you've seen a ghost.

9 What's that noise? It _____ thunder.

10 Their new perfume doesn't _____ the old one. It's much sweeter.

VOCABULARY

3 Adjectives for the senses

Find 20 adjectives in the wordsearch. Look in all directions.

G	C	D	T	S	M	A	R	T	S	N	M
S	O	V	G	D	I	M	E	Z	O	C	Q
S	M	A	M	A	A	F	T	X	U	R	W
E	F	Z	V	M	S	T	T	C	R	U	E
L	O	A	P	P	E	T	I	Z	I	N	G
E	R	O	U	G	H	Y	B	C	J	C	R
T	T	H	T	A	S	T	Y	V	S	H	T
S	A	K	Y	H	E	S	A	L	T	Y	Y
A	B	C	O	S	Y	P	U	O	R	Y	K
T	L	T	F	O	S	I	I	U	O	U	L
H	E	A	V	Y	F	C	R	D	N	I	I
G	S	P	O	O	K	Y	O	B	G	O	S

4 Opposite adjectives

Write the opposites.

1 dark blue   _____ _____
2 dark hair   _____ _____
3 sweet almonds   _____ _____
4 sweet wine   _____ _____
5 a hard exam   _____ _____
6 a hard bed   _____ _____
7 a hot curry   _____ _____
8 a hot bath   _____ _____
9 old people   _____ _____
10 old cars   _____ _____

5 Use your dictionary: Checking spelling

a Look up the adjectives in your dictionary and correct the spelling.

1 It _____ _____ . ~~scracthy~~ *scratchy*
2 It _____ _____ . *defening*
3 It _____ _____ . *fragant*
4 It _____ _____ . *fruitty*

b Complete the phrases with *looks*, *feels*, etc.

6 Remember words from the text

Complete the words or expressions.

EXAMPLE A small light wind. ____*breeze*____

1 what you use to protect yourself from the sun

   s_____ t_____ l_____

2 put a new product on the market **l**_____

3 working well (*adj.*) **e**_____

4 feeling like doing sth *in the* **m**_____ *for*

5 an idea many people have which is false

   m_____

6 the opposite way *in* **r**_____

7 probable **l**_____

7 Prepositions

Complete with the correct preposition.

1 What's the reason _____ the increase in sales?

2 Supermarkets are cheap compared _____ other shops.

3 The new product will soon be _____ sale.

4 This detergent is identical _____ that one.

5 Playing music in the shop resulted _____ customers staying there longer.

6 Smell has always been regarded _____ the most emotional sense.

7 It's very expensive but _____ the other hand it's more effective.

8 Let's buy this one instead _____ that one.

8 Pronunciation: Linking

Mark where the words are linked in spoken English. Practise saying them.

1 She sounds as if she's got a cold.

2 Your old shoes are looking really scruffy.

3 The lights in my room are too dim.

4 You've bought a lot of apples!

5 Is there anything on at the cinema tonight?

6 Let's invite everyone we know to the party.

READING AND WRITING

9 Reading

a Quickly read the information on world marketing campaigns. What was the main reason for the problems?

The *Nova* Awards
★ ★ ★ ★ ★ **IN COMMUNICATION**

The title of these annual awards comes from General Motors' unsuccessful attempt to market their *Nova* car in Latin America. They thought that Nova in English made the car sound like 'new' and 'innovative'. Unfortunately the car did not sell well due to the fact that *no va*, in Spanish, means 'it doesn't go' or 'it's broken'. However, GM are not the only company to have had translation problems. Here are some others:

⭐ The Canadian beer company, *Coors*, translated its slogan, *Turn it loose* into Spanish, where it was read as 'Suffer From Diarrhoea'.

⭐ *Clairol* introduced the *Mist Stick,* a hair accessory, into Germany, only to find out that *mist* is German slang for 'animal excrement'.

⭐ Pepsi's slogan, *Come alive with the Pepsi generation* unfortunately translated into Chinese as 'Pepsi brings your ancestors back from the grave'.

⭐ The Coca Cola name in China was first read as *Kekoukela* meaning 'bite the wax tadpole'. Coke then researched 40,000 characters to find a phonetic equivalent, *Kokou Kole*, which translates as 'happiness in the mouth'.

⭐ When Parker Pen marketed a ball-point pen in Mexico, its adverts should have read, in Spanish, 'It won't leak in your pocket and embarrass you.' The company thought that the word *embarazar* meant 'to embarrass'. Unfortunately, it means 'to make pregnant'.

Glossary	
bring back from the grave	make alive again
wax	material from which candles are made
tadpole	a baby frog
stuffed with	filled with
leak	lose liquid

b Read the article again carefully with the glossary and write the name of the company.

Who …

1 didn't realize that their product name had an unfortunate informal meaning in another language?   _____

2 used a slogan which reminded people of an unpleasant medical condition?   _____

3 thought that a word in a foreign language would mean the same as a similar English word?   _____

4 used a name which sounded like a two-word phrase in another language?   _____

5 used a slogan which reminded people of the supernatural?   _____

6 had problems finding a name in another language which sounded good and had an acceptable meaning?   _____

10 Writing: Letter of complaint

Complete the letter of complaint with the sentences (A–H

A he totally ignored me.
B In view of the poor service of your staff
C I look forward to hearing from you.
D I am writing to complain
E as I had requested.
F to my great embarrassment.
G I also hope that you will take note of my comments
H by which time they were completely cold.

Dear Sir/Madam,

¹☐ about the meal I had in your restaurant last night, Tuesday 25th May.

First of all, the table in the private room had not been booked for us ²☐ Instead we had to sit at a small table at the back of the restaurant. The service was slow and the starters took an hour to arrive at our table, ³☐ Another hour passed before we were served our main course and most of what we had ordered was quite inedible. When I tried to complain to the waiter, ⁴☐ My business colleagues by this stage were getting extremely restless, ⁵☐ We left without having either dessert or coffee, which we ordered in the bar of their hotel.

⁶☐ and the inadequate quality of the food we were served, I am requesting a full refund of the meal. ⁷☐ and improve the standard of your restaurant.

⁸☐

Yours faithfully,

Mr R. Grubb

Made in the USA

> 'I like to be in America, OK by me in America. Everything's free in America …'
> *(from West Side Story) Stephen Sondheim, US songwriter*

GRAMMAR

1 CHECK WHAT YOU KNOW: The passive

a Revise the rules. Then do exercise **b**.

Use	Example	Notes/Problems
Use the passive when the focus of a sentence is **on the thing/person that is the object** of an action instead of on the thing/person that does the action.	*The film was made in 1990. Rice is grown in Japan. In Britain camera films are sold in chemist's.*	(= we are interested in the film, not in the director, etc.) ❶ The passive is often used in English where other languages use an impersonal verb. ❶ The passive is more common in written than in spoken English.
If the person who did the action is also important use *by*.	*The new building was opened by the Prime Minister.*	

b Complete the text with the verbs in the passive in the correct tense.

Marty's Clothing Company

¹ _____ (set up) three years ago by my brother-in-law. He decided that the goods would ² _____ (make) in South America and then ³ _____ (export) to Europe.

A small profit ⁴ _____ (make) in the first year, but the next year there were huge losses and my brother-in-law ⁵ _____ (declare) bankrupt. Unfortunately the debt is so big that he ⁶ _____ just _____ (arrest).

At the moment he ⁷ _____ (hold) at the local police station. His case ⁸ _____ (hear) in the Magistrate's Court next week. We're hoping he ⁹ _____ (release) but if he's found guilty he might ¹⁰ _____ (send) to prison.

2 NEW LANGUAGE: *It* + passive + clause

Change the sentences into the passive to make them sound more formal.

EXAMPLE People think that someone murdered him.
It is thought that he was murdered.

1 People say that crimes committed by young people are increasing.

   It _____

2 Some people think that TV programmes and video games are to blame.

   It _____

3 People hope that the government will take action.

   It _____

4 People have said they are planning to ban all violent programmes.

   It _____

5 However, nobody thinks this will happen in the near future.

   It _____

3 Passives with two objects

Rewrite the sentences to change the focus.

1 Her mother is teaching her French.

   She _____

2 The managing director gave the workers some bad news.

   The workers _____

3 The director has offered the staff a pay increase.

   The staff _____

4 My colleagues promised me their support.

   I _____

5 They sent my sister the clothes she had ordered.

   My sister _____

VOCABULARY

4 Business people and organizations

Decide if the word in **bold** is right ✓ or wrong ✗. If it is wrong, change it.

EXAMPLE A group of shops, hotels, etc. owned by the same person is a ~~company~~. ✗ _chain_

1 A **multinational company** has offices in many countries. ☐ _____

2 A person to whom a company belongs is the **manager**. ☐ _____

3 The group of people who work for a particular organization are the **staff**. ☐ _____

4 Someone who receives professional services from a lawyer, etc. is a **customer**. ☐ _____

5 A **client** is a person who works with you.
   ☐ _____

6 A shop or factory which produces or sells goods is a **business**. ☐ _____

7 A person who has an important position in a company is an **executive**. ☐ _____

8 The person who controls part of an organization is the **manager**. ☐ _____

9 A person, company or product that is competing with you is a **competitor**. ☐ _____

10 A person who buys sth, e.g. from a shop is a **colleague**. ☐ _____

5 Use your dictionary: GB/US English

Use your dictionary to complete the chart.

British English	American English
1 *fridge*	icebox
2	elevator
3	faucet
4	closet
5	garbage
6	pants
7	drapes

6 Remember words from the text

Match the formal words and phrases from the text with the synonyms.

1 It is widely thought
2 alter
3 aim for
4 above average
5 It is regarded as
6 shape sth
7 give birth to sth
8 spread sth
9 worldwide

a influence the way sth develops
b all over the world
c change
d Many people think
e intend to do/achieve sth
f extend to a larger area or bigger group of people
g produce or start sth
h People think of it as
i more than usual

7 Pronunciation

Underline the stressed syllable of the word in **bold**.

1 There has been an **increase** in the crime rate.

2 Workers have decided to **protest** about the threat of redundancy.

3 You'll need a work **permit**.

4 All the fruit they eat is **imported**.

5 When the thief began to **insult** the policeman, he was arrested.

6 They gave me a **refund** for that dress.

7 Few countries **produce** enough food to be completely self-sufficient.

8 My teacher told me that I was making great **progress**.

READING AND WRITING

8 Reading

a Read the paragraphs quickly. What, according to the author (American writer, Bill Bryson), are the two reasons why a lot of American food doesn't taste as good as European food?

Star quality?

Ⓐ Now, there is nothing wrong with *Starbucks*, but there's nothing all that special either. The impression you get is that *Starbucks*' principal motivating force is not to produce the finest coffees but to produce more *Starbucks* coffee bars. ☐

Ⓑ The main reason is cost. Everything in America is determined on cost, far more than in other countries. If price is a factor between competing businesses (and it always is) then the cheaper business will inevitably drive out the more expensive one. This rarely leads to improved quality. Actually, it never leads to improved quality. ☐

Ⓒ It is certainly true that a lot of American foodstuffs, white bread, most cheeses, nearly all convenience foods, most beers and coffees, are not as full of flavour or as varied as their counterparts in Europe. Why is this? ☐

Ⓓ The second reason is that Americans are very attached to uniformity. That is, they actually like things to be the same wherever they go. ☐

Ⓔ Take the example of *Starbucks*, a chain of coffee shops in America. They started quietly in Seattle some years ago, but in the last five years the number of its shops has grown to 1,270, and the number is intended to double in the next two years. Already in many cities if you are looking for a coffee bar the choice is almost *Starbucks* or nothing. ☐

b Read the paragraphs again more carefully and number them 1–5.

c Tick ☑ the sentences that the writer agrees with.

1 American food doesn't taste as good as European food. ☐

2 A business which sells cheaper products will do better than one whose products are more expensive. ☐

3 The cheaper something is, the worse quality it will be. ☐

4 Americans like to have a good choice of products or services. ☐

5 In two years' time, *Starbucks* will have twice as many coffee shops. ☐

6 *Starbucks* coffee is delicious. ☐

7 *Starbucks* is not interested in producing good coffee. ☐

9 Writing: For or against?

a Read through the composition once. Don't worry about the gaps. Is it **for** or **against** fast food?

. . . .

Fast food – a better way of eating?

1 _____ , when you walk down the main street of any big city, you see fast food restaurants everywhere. These restaurants, 2 _____ everyone has eaten at some time, have 3 _____ and disadvantages.

The 4 _____ advantage is that a fast-food meal is, 5 _____ the name implies, quick. This is perfect for modern life, where time is essential. Secondly, they are relatively cheap, 6 _____ is important, especially for young people 7 _____ don't have much money to spend. Thirdly, many people find fast food tasty, and enjoy eating it.

8 _____ it seems as if there are many things in favour of fast food, the disadvantages are perhaps more serious. 9 _____ to traditional food, fast food is very unhealthy – in fact, it is responsible for the obesity problem in many developed countries.

In conclusion, though fast food may be cheaper and quicker than traditional food, I think that the disadvantages are more important and I 10 _____ avoid eating it.

. . . .

b Complete the composition with a word or expression from the list.

advantages	although	as
compared	main	nowadays
personally	where	which	who

Shakespeare in business?

> 'All the world's a stage, and all the men and women merely players.'
> *William Shakespeare, English dramatist*

GRAMMAR

1 NEW LANGUAGE: *so* and *such*

a Cross out the incorrect form.

1 That company is *so/such* successful it's going to become the market leader.

2 I'm tired because I've had *so/such* a busy day.

3 I won't forget your birthday because you've reminded me *so/such* many times.

4 My sister's *so/such* lazy – she doesn't help in the house at all.

5 My in-laws are *so/such* nice people – I get on really well with them.

6 We would have gone to that school if the fees hadn't been *so/such* high.

7 I love your living room. It's *so/such* cosy!

8 My house is always in *so/such* a mess after the weekend.

9 This silk shirt was *so/such* a bargain!

b Join the sentences with *so* or *such* (a) + *that*.

1 His trousers were too tight. He couldn't sit down.

His _____

_____

2 It was a really bad joke. Nobody laughed.

It _____

_____

3 They were inexperienced climbers. They needed rescuing.

They _____

_____

4 There were a lot of different brands. I didn't know which to choose.

There were _____

_____

5 My niece is a very shy girl. Everyone makes fun of her.

My niece _____

_____

6 My neighbours made a terrible noise. I couldn't get to sleep.

My neighbours _____

_____

2 End-of-book revision

Read the text quickly once. Then write one word in each gap.

. . . .

By next week I'll ^{1}_____ had my new computer for exactly a year, but I still don't know how ^{2}_____ get the most out of it. I'm one of those people ^{3}_____ can switch the thing on and type, but my knowledge stops there. The more symbols I see telling me about all the wonderful things I should be able to do, ^{4}_____ more useless I feel. I know it's my fault. I ^{5}_____ have done a course when I was at school. But at the time I thought it was something I could teach myself. I must have ^{6}_____ crazy!

So when I saw the advert ^{7}_____ the course, I immediately applied to do it. It looked ^{8}_____ if it had been designed for me personally! It promised ^{9}_____ teach you all the computer skills I knew I lacked. I turned ^{10}_____ early on the first day, full of enthusiasm. We were shown into a large room where there were at least fifty computers, enough for ^{11}_____ person to have their own. I sat down and waited for the teacher to appear. After a while I realized that ^{12}_____ except me was already typing away. I looked at the screen and it said, 'Welcome to the course. I am your personal tutor. Press any key to continue.' So that was it. There was ^{13}_____ teacher to sympathetically explain to me ^{14}_____ I was doing wrong. Just another screen full of symbols for me to get lost in. If I'd known that it was going to be like that, I ^{15}_____ never have done the course!

. . . .

VOCABULARY

3 Abstract nouns

Form the abstract noun of these words and write them in the correct column.

ambitious   appreciate   ~~bored~~   child   complain   free   guilty   happy
leader   long   mature   neighbour   relation   responsible   strong   weak

-dom	-ity	-ness	-tion
boredom			

-th	-t	-hood	-ship

4 Revision: Crossword

Across

2 Don't leave your clothes on the floor! _____ them _____ !
4 I'm really looking _____ to the party!
7 a small carpet
10 If you want to remember a phone number, _____ it down.
11 the part at the end of the body of an animal, fish, etc
12 another verb for manage (a company)
14 in the end, after difficulty
17 the thing you turn on for water to come out
18 a phrasal verb which means establish or start (e.g. a business)
19 the opposite of loose
22 the top part of a house
24 to give hope, support or confidence to sb

Down

1 the opposite of victory
2 the opposite of patterned
3 the piece of paper a doctor gives you to get medicine
5 If you owe sb money you are in _____ .
6 Someone who treats people unfairly, especially women, because of their sex has a _____ attitude.
8 A person who always leaves things in a mess is _____ .
9 the process where a judge and jury decide if sb is innocent or guilty
13 the area where you live
15 an insect which has the reputation of being hard-working
16 a portable computer
20 an animal which gives milk but is not a cow
21 If you have a good relationship with sb, you _____ on with them.
23 a common virus where you have a cold and a temperature

5 Revision: Word-building

Complete the sentences with the correct form of the word in brackets.

1 I love New York, _____ in the autumn. (special)

2 He only reads _____ books, never novels. (science)

3 The opposite of a democracy is a _____ . (dictator)

4 Those jeans look great. They're really _____ . (fashion)

5 They're obviously wealthy. Their house is really _____ . (luxury)

6 African elephants are in danger of _____ . (extinct)

READING

6 Reading

a Read the article quickly. Who did Shakespeare spend the end of his life with?

Shakespeare's love life

Romeo and Juliet is the greatest love story ever written. It was inspired, according to the film *Shakespeare In Love*, by the writer's own passionate affair with the beautiful daughter of a rich Elizabethan merchant. The screenwriters admit, however, that their story is fiction. So what is the truth about William Shakespeare's love life?

Despite being the most famous Englishman in the world, very little is known for certain about Shakespeare's private life. We know he married Anne Hathaway at Stratford-upon-Avon in 1582 when he was 18 and she was three months pregnant. Yet when he was 24 he had already left her at home and moved to London, attracted by the world of the theatre. Unfortunately, just as he arrived, the theatres were being closed because of the terrible plague epidemic which hit London, so he turned to poetry as a way to explore his own creativity.

The intensity of the poetry suggests a real woman with whom Shakespeare was in love. We can imagine that he was not faithful to Anne Hathaway in Stratford because of the passion in his work, but Shakespeare names no names. Unless a love letter turns up, signed and addressed to his lover, we will never know if there really was another woman.

We do know of one episode in Shakespeare's life which proves his success with women. During the performance of Richard III, a woman in the audience fell in love with the leading actor Richard Burbage and went backstage to arange a meeting later that evening. However, Shakespeare overheard their plans and got to the meeting first. He charmed the lady and joked to Burbage when he arrived later: 'William the Conqueror comes before Richard III.'

Shakespeare left London for Stratford in 1612 to spend the rest of his life with the woman he had married before he became famous. However, the question of who provided the inspiration for his work still remains unanswered, as the identity of his lover in London is still unknown.

b Mark the sentences **T** (true) or **F** (false).

1 *Romeo and Juliet* was inspired by Shakespeare's affair with the daughter of a rich merchant. ☐

2 Shakespeare is better-known than any other Englishman. ☐

3 He married Anne Hathaway when she was expecting a child. ☐

4 He moved to London with his wife in 1588. ☐

5 When he arrived in London, the theatre was just becoming popular. ☐

6 Shakespeare's plays were unsuccessful, so he turned to poetry. ☐

7 We know he had lovers because of love letters he received. ☐

8 Shakespeare once spent a romantic evening with a member of the audience who had fallen in love with him. ☐

9 He spent his last years with his wife. ☐

10 Anne Hathaway probably provided the inspiration for his work. ☐

LISTENING

1 A personal view

a Quickly re-read Bill Bryson's article about *Starbucks* coffee shops on page 69.

b **T7.1** Listen to Debbie, an American, giving her opinion on the article. What is the only thing she agrees with him about?

c Listen again and choose the best answer a, b, or c.

1 Debbie has mixed feelings about the article because
   a she doesn't like the writer's sense of humour.
   b she's American herself.
   c she doesn't like stereotypes.

2 Debbie thinks that
   a other countries copy America.
   b cost is more important in America than Europe.
   c Americans don't like variety.

3 Debbie's partner
   a doesn't drink coffee.
   b likes *Starbucks* coffee.
   c thinks there are too many *Starbucks*.

4 Debbie's main criticism of the writer is that
   a he hasn't tried *Starbucks* coffee himself.
   b he hasn't tried all their different varieties of coffee.
   c he doesn't talk about their different varieties of coffee.

2 My favourite Shakespeare play

a **T7.2** Listen to four people talking about their favourite Shakespeare play. Write the number of the speaker next to the play they mention.

A Midsummer Night's Dream ☐   *Othello* ☐

The Merchant of Venice ☐   *Hamlet* ☐

Romeo and Juliet ☐   *The Tempest* ☐

b Listen again and match the sentences to the speakers. There is one extra sentence you do not need to use.

Who …

a enjoyed seeing an amateur production of their favourite play? ☐

b enjoys love stories? ☐

c thinks the message of the play is enjoyable even today? ☐

d enjoyed acting in a Shakespeare play? ☐

e had a personal experience which made the play more relevant? ☐

PRONUNCIATION

1 Linking words

a Mark where the words are linked in spoken English.

1 I wouldn't like to run an international company.
2 Our competitors are launching a new product in April.
3 There's a chain of restaurants with three branches in the centre.
4 He made an enormous profit in only two and a half years.
5 The owner of our school lives abroad.

b **T7.3** Listen and repeat. Practise saying them as quickly as possible.

2 Long and short vowels

a Underline the long vowel sounds.

1 The lead singer lives in Leeds.
2 Her father had a heart transplant.
3 What's the dog got in his paw? Is it a thorn?
4 Her computer stopped working on the first of March.
5 Look! You've dropped food on your new suit!

b **T7.4** Listen and repeat. Focus on making the difference between the long and short vowel sounds.

3 Sentence stress: Weak forms

a **T7.5** Listen and write the missing words. Then listen and repeat the sentences.

1 _____ supermarket chain _____ founded _____ _____ States.
2 _____ colleague _____ mine _____ _____ arrested _____ theft.
3 _____ staff _____ told _____ work overtime.
4 _____ found _____ factory _____ _____ make _____ product.
5 _____ company's going _____ _____ taken over _____ _____ multinational.

FILE 1

T1.1

A So, Caroline, how long have you been playing the violin?

B I started when I was about three. Both of my parents were musicians, although not professional ones. They obviously influenced me a lot, but the thing that really made me want to learn was when my older sister started having piano lessons. I liked listening to her, though I had to sit very quietly, and of course soon I was asking if I could learn to play an instrument myself, and my parents bought me a second-hand violin.

A Who did you have lessons with?

B My mother taught me first, until I was about five or six, and then I started going to a private teacher. I loved the lessons, but getting there was an absolute nightmare as the teacher lived miles away and we didn't have a car, so it was half an hour on the bus and then I had to walk for ages carrying my violin, which was really heavy. Then when I was twelve I joined a youth orchestra and began playing with other young musicians.

A How much did you practise a day?

B When I was younger, about half an hour or so, but it gradually increased as I got better, till when I was twelve or thirteen I was doing maybe a couple of hours a day.

A Was that a problem – I mean didn't it affect your school work or social life?

B Well, not so much my schoolwork, but my social life, yes. In fact when I was 15 I rebelled and told my parents that I'd had enough and I didn't want to go on with the violin. All my friends used to go out in the evening and at weekends and I could hardly ever go with them because either I had to practise or I had the youth orchestra or something. I just wanted to have a normal teenager's life.

A How did your parents react to this?

B Well, they were really disappointed but they were also incredibly understanding, though obviously they thought it was a mistake. But they said right, you can give it up, so for a while I stopped completely.

A So what made you change your mind?

B Well, after about two months, I realized I was missing playing the violin so I told my parents I wanted to take it up again. Since then I've never looked back. I mean, I know now it's what I want to do as a career, be a soloist or, if I'm not good enough, play in a professional orchestra.

A Do you feel different from other teenagers?

B Well yes, I mean, mainly because most teenagers are not that interested in classical music – all my school friends are into pop music. But I don't mind now, in fact I quite like being different.

T1.2

1 I'm a chemist, and I've been working for a large American chemical company called D–O–W since I left university. Now I'm based in Holland in a town in the province of Zeeland. I work on the development of new chemical products and other projects. I've been here for six and a half years now and before that I spent four and a half years in Germany. I picked up the language quite quickly, as German and Dutch are so similar, but when the company suggested I learnt French as well, I started having problems.

The biggest difference I've noticed is the people here are much more direct than in Britain. They always say exactly what they mean, which can come across as being impolite to the British, whereas really they're just being open – being honest.

Although I miss my family and friends, I don't think I'll be going back to Britain in the near future, especially as I've just bought a house with my Dutch girlfriend not far from where I work.

2 At the moment we're living in Auckland, the largest city in New Zealand. We don't live in the city itself, but in a suburb on the north shore.

I'm here with my husband, Tom, who's a sales engineer. He goes travelling around Asia a lot with his job, so I spend most of my time looking after our six-year-old son, Jack. I don't work as I haven't got a work permit.

The biggest difference between New Zealand and Britain for me is that New Zealand is so empty! There are about four million people here compared to 60 million back home, so everything is fairly empty and a lot of New Zealand is very rural. Another difference is that there aren't any historical buildings here, I suppose because it's still a relatively new country. When we tell people that our house in Britain is about 400 years old, they don't believe us!

We've been here for about two years now and we're going home in April next year. I'm quite looking forward to it, as I've really missed my family and friends.

3 We live in a small village near Oslo in Norway and we manage an organic farm. My husband looks after the business side of things and I'm responsible for selling our products. We've been here for over nine years now and things are getting easier. I really enjoy the work, but it's quite difficult getting used to life in the country, especially when you are living abroad.

The biggest difference for me between Norway and Britain is that people here take life a lot more seriously. They don't laugh at themselves as much as we do. They don't have as much of a sense of humour. The other big difference is the winter. It's so long and dark, and of course it snows a lot. Every year I can't wait for spring to come.

Despite the differences, I'm getting on OK here and we've met some really nice people. There's not much point in me going back to Britain, as I've now got more friends here than there, although I do miss my family, especially as we've now got three children. I'm really looking forward to my mum coming over to give us a hand on the farm this spring!

4 I'm living in Seville in southern Spain at the moment, working for a TV production company. I've been here for about eighteen months now, and I'm just about to change my job for the second time. I don't think I'll go back to Britain in the near future, especially as I've got a Spanish girlfriend now. We moved in together two months ago and things are going really well – though of course it's early days …

I think the biggest difference for me living here is the lifestyle. People work longer hours, but they seem to know how to enjoy themselves more – the Spanish are professional partygoers. The only thing that gets me down a bit is that the stereotype about always leaving things till tomorrow – the *mañana* syndrome – really is true here and it can get a bit frustrating at times, like when you want someone to come and fix your toilet. They're not brilliant about things like that in Britain either of course, but I think they are a bit quicker.

T1.4

1 Could you tell me where the bank is?

2 Do you know how to get to the station?

3 Can you tell me if this train goes to London?

4 Do you know how long it takes to get there?

5 Could you tell me if there's a restaurant near here?

FILE 2

A We've all heard of acupuncture but very few of us have had any first-hand experience of it. Dr Chang, first of all can you tell us, what exactly is acupuncture?

B Acupuncture is a very old technique, which uses needles to prevent or treat illness. It has been practised for over 2500 years in China, which is of course where it came from. It is part of the system of traditional Chinese medicine, where health is seen as a constantly changing flow of energy or 'qi', as we call it in Chinese. Changes in the flow of energy is what causes people to become ill or suffer from health problems. Acupuncture helps to control these changes.

A And how does acupuncture work?

B Well, I'll try to explain it as simply as I can. The Chinese believe that 'qi', the energy that is, flows through the body through 14 channels. To make the energy flow more strongly, an acupuncturist inserts a number of tiny sterile needles just under the skin in places called acupoints. There are thousands of acupoints in the human body, and each one is associated with a specific internal organ or a system of organs. For example, if you've got a stomach-ache, we might insert needles into acupoints on your hand. Or if you've got a problem with your eyesight, we might put needles in the acupoints in your foot.

A So, what could I expect on my first visit to an acupuncturist?

B On the first visit the acupuncturist will ask you about your complete medical history. Then he may take your pulse, look at your tongue and check your blood pressure. You might also have your first treatment during this visit. In general, your visits will take place once or twice a week over several months until your health problem has been solved.

A But don't the needles hurt?

B They can feel uncomfortable at times but no, they very rarely hurt. The needles are very thin and flexible and they are designed to enter the skin easily. An acupuncturist usually uses from one to fifteen needles and they may be left in for 15 to 40 minutes, depending on the patient's problem. In fact, most people find acupuncture sessions relaxing and many of them fall asleep either during or immediately after treatment.

1 When you get to 36, which is what I am now, you have more self-confidence than when you were in your, say, in your twenties or early thirties. You've had the chance to meet a wide variety of people, to do things and see places, which helps you to realize what you want and don't want in life. Physically, I feel very much as I did ten years ago, though I must admit I don't enjoy seeing the first grey hairs and wrinkles. I suppose I'll have to get used to it.

Most people say childhood is the best age, but I think you should always try to find the positive aspects of any age and it's up to you to make it the best. Being a teenager is definitely the worst time. You're in limbo between being a child and being an adult, and you tend to be insecure and easily influenced by others. It's hard for teenagers to find out who they really are.

2 I'm 15 – well, 14 really – but it's my birthday next week. I prefer this age to when I was 12 or 13 because I can go out more with my friends though my parents still make me come home much too early. And at school they treat you with a bit more respect than they used to when we were kids. They give us loads of homework though – I have to do about two hours every night, which I think is much too much, so I can never watch telly during the week. I think you have a much better time when you're 18 because then you've finished school and can do what you like. I get really fed up with my mum and dad telling me what to do all the time.

3 What I like best about being 69 is that I don't have to worry about my children any more because they've all settled down and are living their own lives. The other good thing is that, as I'm not working, I can do what I like, when I like. I don't like the aches and pains, though, and I think things were better when I was 60, and I had just retired – I had more energy to do things than I do now. For me, personally, the worst age was in my early thirties when my children were young and I never got enough sleep or had any time for myself. I just seemed to spend all day cooking meals and doing the washing.

4 I'm really happy with the age I am now, because I'm 22 and I have all the freedom I need without too much responsibility. I'm still studying so I don't have the pressures of work yet, but I'm not a child any more, so my parents trust me to lead my own life. My only problem is not being financially independent and having to depend on my parents for money. My worst age was definitely when I was a teenager. At 16 you're embarrassed and unsure of yourself. I remember feeling very self-conscious then especially about my appearance. And my parents were quite authoritarian – I was always having terrible arguments with them.

1 I'll have finished in a minute.

2 If you don't come now, you'll miss the programme.

3 What will you be doing this time next year?

4 I wouldn't do it if I didn't want to.

5 I'm addicted to that new soap opera.

FILE 3

T3.1

A So, Manolo, I hear you had a terrifying experience in Santo Domingo. What exactly happened?

B Well, as you know, we were there for my company's annual conference. It was mainly work, meetings and so on, but of course we had a bit of free time too. Anyway, one afternoon Jesús, my boss, and I decided to hire some jet-skis and go racing in the sea, out towards where the coral reefs were.

A You're joking! I thought you couldn't swim!

B Well, I'm not very keen on the sea but I can swim, though not very well, and you know, as we were there, it seemed a bit of a pity not to do any water sports. Anyway, we were having a really good time, racing, and fooling around, when suddenly I looked and saw that Jesús had lost his jet-ski, and he was just sort of hanging onto the rocks in the middle of the sea.

A No!

B It turned out that he had decided to have a swim, and hadn't realized how strong the current was, and of course the jet-ski just floated away and eventually sank. But anyway, when I saw what had happened, I realized at once that we had a really serious problem because we were a long way from the beach – much too far to swim back – and also the sea had got much rougher and there were strong currents. And on top of it all, we'd been told that there were sharks on the other side of the reef!

A What an awful situation! What did you do?

B Well, I had to make my mind up quickly. I went towards Jesús with my jet-ski and I tried to pick him up, to get him on the back of my jet-ski. But it was impossible – the sea was too rough and we just couldn't balance and in the end my jet-ski sank too. So there we both were, hanging onto the rocks, wet and cold, being knocked about by the waves, and thinking that that was the end of it for us.

A So how did you get rescued in the end?

B Well, luckily the people on the beach who had rented us the jet-skis realized that we must be having problems because we hadn't come back and they sent a boat to help us.

A So how long did you spend on the rock then?

B Probably only about half an hour or forty minutes, but I can tell you, it was one of the longest half-hours of my life.

A Why didn't you just leave Jesús on the rock and go back to the beach to get help?

B I don't know really. I suppose my first instinct was to try to save him.

A Because he's your boss?

B No, because he's my friend. Maybe if he'd just been my boss, I would have left him there!

T3.2

The group got up early in the morning, left camp 5, and started to climb towards the North Face of Everest. There was very little snow and a mixture of rock and ice, which made it very difficult for them to climb. After about five hours, the group arrived at the area used today as camp 6. They began heading west and soon after, they found a bright blue Chinese oxygen cylinder. At this point they realized they must be near the old Chinese camp. They had originally thought that this would probably be higher up the mountain.

The group then made the decision to all go in different directions. Half an hour later some of the group members found a cemetery of frozen bodies, but all of these were of climbers who had died in more recent expeditions. Then one member of the group, Conred Anker, decided to look a bit lower down. Suddenly he saw a patch of white which was whiter than the rock around it and whiter than the snow. He began climbing towards this whiter patch. When he got closer he saw that it was a body. Not a recent body, but one that had clearly been there for a long time. Most of the clothing had gone and the skin was white, bleached by the sun. It certainly looked like a body that could have been lying there for 75 years – could it be Irvine's body?

But when Andy Politz, another member of the expedition, arrived, he immediately said, 'This isn't Irvine.', which shocked everyone. The group began carefully examining the few clothes left on the body and they found the remains of a laundry label which said G. Mallory. Andy Politz was right – it was not Andrew Irvine. Unexpectedly, they had found the body of his companion, George Mallory, the greatest mountain climber of his generation.

T3.3

1 A I'm going to New York next week.
   B No! Are you?

2 A I've lost my car keys.
   B How annoying!

3 A My sister's having a baby!
   B Wow! That's great.

4 A So then the door opened slowly.
   B And what happened next?

5 A I've got a new job!
   B Really! So have I!

6 A My mother's getting married again.
   B You're joking!

7 A Neither of my suitcases arrived.
   B How awful!

8 A I've got to retake my exams.
   B What a pity!

T3.4

1 My dog was run over by a car yesterday.

2 I've passed all my exams.

3 There's a cow in the garden!

4 My brother's lost his job.

5 The Prime Minister's resigned.

6 I've won a holiday to Australia.

7 It's started to rain again.

8 We won the match! We beat them!

9 I saw Julia Roberts at the airport yesterday.

10 The tickets are all sold out.

T3.5

1 It can't have been me – I wasn't there.

2 You should have phoned.

3 I would have told you if I'd known.

4 You must have finished by now.

5 What would you have done?

6 You might have left it at home.

7 We shouldn't have eaten so much!

8 If it'd been cheaper, I'd have bought it.

FILE 4

T4.1

1 My favourite item of clothing has to be a pair of trousers that I bought in Italy two years ago. They're beige and they're perfect for the hot weather, as the material is very light. I think they're the most comfortable trousers that I've ever worn. The best thing about them is that there are pockets in the legs so that I can keep things like my wallet and my keys in them without worrying about them getting pinched by a pickpocket!

2 I haven't really got one favourite item of clothing, but I do like open-necked sports shirts in general. When I was working I had to wear a suit and tie every day, five days a week, and so now I'm retired, I absolutely *hate* wearing ties. My favourite colour is light blue and I've got a number of polo shirts in that colour. I couldn't say which is my favourite, as I feel comfortable in all of them.

3 My favourite item of clothing is probably a dress I bought a few years ago in a department store in town. I'd been looking for a nice dress for a long time and when I saw this one hanging on the rail, I just had to buy it. When I tried it on, it looked pretty good, so I didn't feel too guilty about the price. Unfortunately, it looks a bit old-fashioned now, so I'll have to look for a new one. I still wear it sometimes though, even though it doesn't look as good as it used to.

4 It's difficult to say which of my clothes I like best. Actually, I like the T-shirt I'm wearing right now because it looks nice and feels really comfortable. I bought it in the sales last summer and it was reduced from a ridiculous price. I buy most of my clothes in the sales because I don't agree with paying so much for something you'll only wear a few times.

T4.2

A Most people today have heard of the Chinese philosophy about house decoration called – well, I've always said *feng shui* – but that's not the correct pronunciation is it, Rebecca?

B No, the correct way of saying it is 'fung shway'.

A Rebecca, you're an expert in *feng shui* [is that right? B Yes, yeah!], but you're now getting very worried about the success it's having. Why is that?

B Well, it seems to me that the industry is getting out of control.
My main worry is that there are so many people around now who claim to be *feng shui* experts and are giving people what they pretend is expert advice. But this advice is often not true and is sometimes very irresponsible. They've started telling people, for example, that the arrangement of their house is going to make them ill, or even worse, make their children ill.

A Who are these so-called experts?

B Well, some of them are just people who see *feng shui* as a good way to make easy money. Others are fanatics who are turning this, this ancient guide to interior design, into something more like a religion. Some of the symbols that *feng shui* encourages people to use are starting to be considered as gods or idols in people's homes. For example, in the *feng shui* philosophy, a 'three-legged frog' figure symbolizes money. But now people are taking such symbols and their meanings much too seriously. I was recently asked by a very worried client, 'Where should I put my frog?', as if he thought that getting rich all depended on where he put his frog.

A *Feng shui* has gone from being a completely new idea for most of us to being a common topic of interior design conversation, hasn't it?

B Yes, and this is exactly where the problem lies. Publishers know that if the words 'feng shui' appear in the title of a book, they're likely to sell more copies. As a result, there are now many different theories of *feng shui* being sold, a lot of which are very different to the original principles. People have got to be able to recognize what is the authentic *feng shui*. It isn't based on feelings of fear and superstition. It is not about how having a window or a bedroom in the wrong place can bring you bad luck and ruin your life. The emphasis has always been on the positive. It is about how the natural energy that is around us all can help us to improve our lives.

T4.4

1 The sooner the better.
2 There's a new block of flats on the corner.
3 I wish the weather would get better.
4 We'll have to have the house decorated.
5 I wish you were a bit more sociable.
6 She's wearing white leather trainers.

FILE 5

T5.1

And to start the programme tonight, the strange rescue story of a gorilla who saved a young child's life. Yesterday in Chicago Zoo, a three-year-old boy was with his family, looking at the gorillas. But while his parents were momentarily distracted, the little boy ran away from them, climbed over a fence, and fell five metres into the gorillas' cage. Inside the cage, there were several adult gorillas, including Binti, an eight-year-old female with an 18-month-old baby. This is a situation in which many female gorillas are often extra aggressive in order to protect their young. The little boy's family and other visitors to the zoo watched in horror as Binti, with her own baby clinging on her back, walked slowly over to the boy, who was lying injured on the ground. But to everyone's amazement, the gorilla didn't attack him. Instead she picked him up, and carefully carried him over to the gate where the zookeepers were able take him to safety. He's now recovering in hospital. A spokeswoman for the zoo said that they had prepared Binti for the birth of her own baby by giving her human dolls to play with. But even with this training, zookeepers were still surprised by how gently she treated the child.

T5.2

1 This happened to me last Christmas. It was about six months after I'd separated from my husband. The separation had been very unpleasant and we weren't speaking to each other or in contact at all at the time. I had tickets for a concert one night and I went with a new friend, someone I'd just started going out with. Well, the doors had just shut and the last people were finding their places, when suddenly I heard my husband's voice saying, 'I think those are our seats.' He was with another woman – in fact one of our neighbours, and they had the two seats next to ours. It was crazy – this huge concert hall and the person I least wanted to see in the world had the seats next to me! I couldn't decide if I should get up and go, but it was too late as the orchestra had already started playing. All four of us sat rigid throughout the concert, just staring straight ahead and without being able to enjoy the music at all. It was the most uncomfortable two hours I've ever had!

2 I was on holiday in Nice a couple of years ago with some friends from university. We were staying at a youth hostel as we were a bit short of money and it was much cheaper than a hotel would have been. One night I had a dream about a schoolfriend who I hadn't seen for years, as he'd moved away and we'd lost contact completely. The next morning, I was queueing to get my breakfast. I'd just picked up my coffee when suddenly, somebody tapped me on the shoulder. I turned round and it was my friend, the one I'd dreamt about. He'd been standing behind me in the queue. I was so amazed I nearly dropped my cup of coffee! It was just such an incredible coincidence after just having the dream!

3 When I first started work, my company sent me to London on a training course for a week. One evening I caught the underground to go back to my hotel for dinner and I bumped into my cousin, who was in the same carriage. This may not sound so incredible, but Sarah lives in Canada and I hadn't heard from her for years. It turned out that she was just in London for a few days as part of a summer trip going round Europe with a friend. It was great to see her and we went for a drink together to make the most of our chance meeting. I haven't seen her since then, and that was ten years ago. Maybe we'll bump into each other again one day when neither of us are expecting it!

4 I had been having some really strong pains in my chest so my doctor sent me to hospital for some tests, you know, just to make sure everything was all right. The tests were quite painful so I was kept in hospital overnight. When I woke up the next morning, I saw there was another patient in the other bed next to me in the ward. We started chatting to each other and then suddenly I realized that I recognized the woman's voice. She had been the sports teacher at the school where my husband had worked years before, and we'd known each other quite well at the time. Since then we'd lost touch, and she'd changed completely as she'd cut her hair and lost a lot of weight, which is why I didn't recognize her at first. It was the last place in the world where I'd have expected to meet up with an old friend!

T5.3

1 How long have you been working here?

2 She's been wearing glasses since she was fifteen.

3 What have you been doing since I last saw you?

4 Have you been living here long?

5 I've been waiting for you for ages.

6 Who's been using my computer?

FILE 6

T6.1

I'd been in Scotland for my summer holidays and I was going to drive back to Paris, where I was working at the time. I was on my own and was going to catch the ferry from Dover to Calais. My ferry was due to leave at 10 in the evening, and I had a couple of hours to kill. I had a quick snack and then I decided to go to a book shop to have a look round. I love spending time in book shops and this particular one is huge – it's on several floors and it closes later than all the other shops, so that meant I would have something to do until I had to get on the boat.

I spent ages looking round all the sections and I found a book I thought I might buy and picked it up. But a bit later I decided not to buy the book, as it was very long and quite heavy to carry. As the section where I had found it was on the third floor, and I was now on the first floor, I just put it on the nearest shelf.

Then I looked at my watch and I realized that it was much later than I thought and that it was time to go to the ferry, so I rushed out of the shop.

The moment I came into the street, I felt a hand on my shoulder and a woman said rather aggressively, 'Excuse me, madam. Can I see the book you've got in your coat pocket?'

I turned round and said, 'What book?' I was feeling really shocked and embarrassed because people had stopped and they were looking at me as if I was a criminal! So I told the woman that I hadn't bought anything, but I'd just been looking. I didn't quite understand what was going on but I imagined that the woman must be a store detective. Anyway, she started looking in my pockets and bag and then I suddenly realized what had happened. She had seen me with the book I had thought about buying, but she hadn't seen me leave it on the shelf. Naturally she thought I had put it in my pocket.

It was a very embarrassing ten minutes until I finally convinced her that I wasn't a shoplifter and that I hadn't got the book. But what was really annoying was the fact that she didn't even apologize when she realized she had made a mistake! If I hadn't been in a hurry to catch the ferry, I would have gone to speak to the manager and ask for an apology.

I eventually caught the ferry and on the crossing, I wrote a letter of complaint to the manager and asked for some kind of compensation for the embarrassing situation I had gone through. Several years later, I'm still waiting for a reply.

T6.2

1 My favourite toy was a teddy bear called Big King, which I've still got, actually. He's sixty-five years old now, as my parents gave him to me for my fifth birthday. Unfortunately, he doesn't look much like the bear they gave me now, as he's lost an eye and one of his legs is almost off.

2 I was very lucky when I was young – and very spoilt – because my grandmother worked in a toyshop, so I had plenty of toys. I suppose my favourite was my Action Man, a doll for boys, dressed as a soldier. I used to play with my sister, who had girl dolls, and we used to pretend that our dolls were going out together. It was all very innocent, of course, but I think, even at that early age, it taught us something about male/female relationships.

3 I still have Bertie in my bedroom, even though he's old and scraggy now and looks like I've had him for years. Well, I have had him for at least fifteen years, as my dad bought him for me once when I was in bed with flu to cheer me up and I must have been five or six then. He's a bright orange cuddly dog, pretty ugly really, but I'm very fond of him.

4 I was mad about Meccano – you know the metal construction toy. I know it's not supposed to be a girl's toy – and in fact it was originally my brother's – but I loved it and we used to spend hours together making all kinds of things, trains, buses, machines. The only thing that was irritating about it was that some of the pieces were really small, especially the screws, and we kept losing them.

T6.3

1 The thief threatened to throw away the diamonds.

2 Although I'd heard it before, I thought it was good.

3 He wasn't thin enough to climb through the window.

4 He deceived me – I thought he was telling the truth.

5 My father taught me to be tough.

6 My daughter's got a rather bad cough.

7 The car thief laughed when he was caught.

8 It's not worth swimming – the sea's too rough.

9 Try to breathe through your mouth.

10 There are three trees in the garden.

T6.5

1 A What do people often wear over their pyjamas?
   B A dressing-gown.

2 A Where can you have an open fire?
   B In a fireplace.

3 A What do you call a letter you send from your computer?
   B An e-mail.

4 A What are people who sell heroin accused of?
   B Drug dealing.

5 A What sentence might a judge give a murderer?
   B A life sentence.

6 A Where can you go to see a doctor?
   B To a health centre.

7 A Where can you see wild animals apart from in a zoo?
   B In a safari park.

8 A What do people often wear to do sport?
   B A tracksuit.

FILE 7

T7.1

A So, Debbie, how did you feel when you read the article?

B Well, I've got mixed feelings really. It's obviously taking a humorous look at things in the States, which is fine, and of course Bill Bryson, who wrote it, is American himself. But I feel uncomfortable with generalizing about nationalities – and in any case I don't agree with everything he says.

A Like what for example?

B Well, I don't know that the first part is true, about cost being more important in America than almost anywhere else. I think that's true everywhere. After all, isn't American capitalism the model Europe, for example, is trying to imitate? I'm also not sure that all Americans like everything to be the same all the time. I guess it depends on the person really.

A What about the example Bill Bryson gives of *Starbucks* coffee shops? I mean, I'm sure you've tried their coffee.

B Actually, I haven't, because I don't drink coffee. Sure, it's true what he says that they're everywhere; you can't go round a corner without seeing one, that I do have to admit. But my partner, who drinks coffee all the time, he's quite keen on their coffee.

A But is it true that their coffee always tastes the same?

B Well, I don't know about that but he's never said so. But my main criticism of the article is that the writer didn't mention the variety of coffee you can drink at a *Starbucks* coffee shop. They offer about twenty different kinds of coffee, all different flavours, like with cream, cappuccino, latte, macchiato, chocolate flavoured – you name it. I don't think many other coffee bars have as much variety.

T7.2

1 I think the only Shakespeare play I've ever read was *The Merchant of Venice*, which I studied at school for an English exam. I quite enjoyed it actually, though I found it a bit difficult to understand. The thing I like most about it is the message. It's really against greed, and people who want more money than they need. I think it's sort of saying that if you try to get too much, you'll end up with nothing in the end. That's how I understood it, anyway. Maybe all bank managers should read it!

2 I'm a bit of a romantic so my favourite Shakespeare play has to be *Romeo and Juliet*. I've seen it at the theatre twice and it was also made into a film, which was very well done. I must admit though that I find the deaths of the two lovers at the end is just a bit too tragic to believe. But I think the language Shakespeare uses when he refers to love is really beautiful and I suppose that's why I like this play so much.

3 I haven't read much Shakespeare but my favourite play is definitely *The Tempest*. I love the way the sea and the weather are such an important part of the play. I spent some time as a sailor in the Navy when I was younger, so I suppose I can understand and enjoy this play better because of my own experience.

4 A few years ago I saw a production of *Midsummer Night's Dream* at my son's secondary school. I don't think I've ever laughed so much in my life, especially the scene where one of the characters turns into a donkey – it was really funny! That's why I much prefer this kind of play, Shakespeare's comedies that is, to his tragedies like *Hamlet*, where everybody seems to die in the end.

1 A

1 1 wakes up 2 give up 3 was over 4 threw away
5 hold on 6 pick up 7 turn down 8 went out

2 1 out of 2 forward to 3 down on 4 on, with

3 1 I look like her.
2 You must cross them out.
3 Switch it off when the film finishes.
4 My mother looks after her when I'm at work.
5 Send it back if you don't like it.
6 Look through it before you sign it.
7 Turn it up. I can't hear it.
8 My son takes after him.

4 **b** b 1 decrease c 2 depart
d 1 make disappear e 1 increase
f 3 stop completely g 3 connect

5 **Text 1:** 1 irrelevant 2 aware 3 tend
Text 2: 1 make 2 mind(s) 3 account

6 1 decision 2 tendency 3 association 4 choice
5 success 6 affection 7 advice 8 comparison

7 **a** 1 like 2 after 3 after 4 on 5 up 6 up
b 1 get up 2 get in 3 get on 4 get off 5 get on

8 1 stereotype 2 applicant 3 tendency 4 research
5 old-fashioned 6 glamorous 7 irrelevant 8 attitude
9 association 10 effect 11 aware 12 account
13 contradict 14 unpopular 15 dramatic

9 **a** They usually meet at Christmas and occasions like
weddings.

b 1 C 2 D 3 B 4 A

c 1 bride 2 get over 3 take place 4 choir 5 tears
6 issue 7 baptism 8 etiquette

10 Paragraph 1 starts: In one family I know …
Paragraph 2 starts: The first and most important
disadvantage …
Paragraph 3 starts: On the other hand, …
Paragraph 4 starts: In conclusion, …

1 B

1 1 Do you now what their latest album is called?
2 Can you remember who wrote the lyrics for
American Pie?
3 Could you tell me if this bus goes to Chelsea?
4 Do you remember where their house is?
5 Can you tell me when the box office closes?
6 Do you know whether (or not) he's coming (or not)?

2 **a** 1 What about? 2 Where to? 3 How long for?
4 What for? 5 Who with? 6 Who to?

b 2 Where is he going to? 3 How long is he going for?
4 What is he going for? 5 Who is he having the
interview with? 6 Who can/do I sell it/the ticket to?

3 1 (✗) Who **wrote** this awful article? 2 (✗) How many
people **do you think** like violent films? 3 (✓)
4 (✗) Which newspaper **uses** the most dramatic headlines?
5 (✗) What **did the papers say** about the film? 6 (✓)
7 (✓) 8 (✗) Which presenter **do you like** best?

4 **a** 1 set 2 directed 3 plot 4 based 5 starred
6 played 7 parts 8 cast

b 1 soundtrack 2 special effects 3 scene
4 dubbed 5 shoot

5 1 audience figures 2 documentary 3 headlines
4 biased 5 tabloid 6 journalist 7 broadcast
8 chat show 9 viewer 10 soap opera
Mystery word: censorship

6 1 on 2 in 3 on 4 on 5 on 6 in

7 1 comedy 2 photographer 3 cartoons 4 fake
5 censorship 6 audience

8 **a** She is against the use of cameras in the courtroom
because she feels it is the law and not television that
should decide if someone is innocent or guilty.

b 1 F 2 T 3 T 4 T 5 F 6 F 7 F 8 T

9 1 What's on TV tonight? 2 What/Which channel is it on?
3 What's it called? 4 What's it about? 5 Where's it set?
6 How long does it last? 7 Who's in it?
8 When does it start?

1 C

1 **b** 1 (✗) carefully 2 (✓) 3 (✗) well 4 (✗) fast
5 (✓) 6 (✗) daily 7 (✓) 8 (✓) 9 (✗) extremely
10 (✗) actually

c 1 ~~nervous~~/nervously 2 ~~good~~/well 3 ~~careful~~/carefully
4 ~~perfect~~/perfectly 5 quiet/~~quietly~~ 6 ~~bad~~/badly

2 1 **Last week** Jenny went to the hairdresser's.
Jenny went to the hairdresser's **last week**.
2 I'm **very** sorry about the accident.
3 You should **never** swim in cold water after a heavy meal.
4 She speaks French and she's **also** good at German.
5 **Ideally** we want to set off early.
We want to set off early, **ideally**.
6 **Usually** prices go up during the summer.
Prices **usually** go up during the summer.
7 I'm **quite** sure I left my keys at home.
8 The paparazzi **even** followed them into the hotel.

3 1 ~~near~~/nearly/almost
2 eventually/in the end/~~at the end~~
3 far/much/~~fairly~~
4 incredibly/extremely/~~slightly~~
5 a little/slightly/~~very~~
6 in fact/actually/~~nowadays~~
7 completely/quite/~~rather~~
8 At the moment/Right now/~~Actually~~

4 1 sense of humour 2 comedian 3 laugh 4 joke
5 funny 6 witty 7 make fun of 8 fun
9 pulling their leg

5 2 Gradually 3 specially 4 Obviously 5 Anyway
6 Apparently 7 Basically 8 actually

6 **b** 1 mood 2 enjoyable 3 course 4 Foreigners
5 strangers 6 career 7 funny, humour

7 **a** He thinks we laugh as a means of communication;
laughter can signal surprise but also relief.

b 1 b 2 b 3 c 4 a

8 1 extremely 2 yesterday 3 early 4 fast
5 eventually 6 immediately 7 Unfortunately
8 Luckily/At that moment 9 at that moment/luckily
10 just

Listening

1 a Yes, she has always wanted to play the violin.

b 1 c 2 b 3 a 4 b

2 a and **b**

Mike (✗) Zeeland, Holland, works for a chemical company, 6½ years, the people are more direct and open

Cathy (✓) Auckland, New Zealand, looks after her son, 2 years, New Zealand is empty and rural and has no historical buildings

Susan (✗) near Oslo, Norway, manages an organic farm, over 9 years, people in Norway take life more seriously; the winter is long and dark and it snows a lot

Luke (✗) Seville, Southern Spain, works for a TV production company, 18 months, people work longer hours but know how to enjoy themselves more; it takes a long time to get things fixed

Pronunciation

3 a 1 pseudonym 2 overcome 3 tendency
4 performance 5 chorus 6 stereotype
7 sensational 8 fortunately 9 automatically
10 especially

2 A

1 b 1 I'll try 2 it would hurt 3 you didn't smoke
4 you don't stop 5 there were 6 isn't
7 will be here 8 weren't/wasn't 9 She won't go

2 a 1 … I **won't** watch it any more.
2 … as soon as he **gets** the results of his tests.
3 (✓)
4 They**'ll make up their minds** as soon as …
5 (✓)
6 If your headache **gets** worse, …
7 … in case **I need** it.
8 (✓)

b 1 ~~when~~/until 2 as soon as/~~unless~~ 3 ~~in case~~/when
4 ~~if~~/in case 5 If/~~Unless~~ 6 unless/~~in case~~

3 a 1 prescription 2 diagnosis 3 x-ray 4 stroke
5 health centre 6 overdose 7 pregnant 8 symptom

b 1 sneezing 2 cough 3 make an appointment
4 GP 5 virus 6 days off 7 acupuncture
8 side effects 9 put on 10 lose weight

4 1 **put** your foot in it 2 **see** eye to eye
3 **give/lend** me a hand 4 **keep** an eye on
5 **goes** in one ear and out the other
6 **keep** my fingers crossed

5 1 ache 2 cure 3 hangover 4 chronic 5 surgeon
6 swollen 7 dizzy 8 ward

6 a Men don't go to the doctor as often as women:
1 because they think they are immortal.
2 because they think it's a sign of weakness.
3 because doctors' surgeries are not male-friendly places.

b 1 C 2 A 3 D 4 B

c 1 put off 2 turn up 3 back up 4 comes to 5 set
up 6 get through to sb

7 1 But/~~Besides~~ 2 ~~Firstly~~/The main advantage
3 In addition/~~However~~ 4 ~~as well~~/also
5 On the other hand/~~Secondly~~ 6 ~~But~~/Besides
7 To sum up/~~At the end~~

2 B

1 b 1 is going to affect/will affect
2 I'm meeting
3 I'm going to change
4 I'll help
5 You'll hit/You're going to hit
6 I'll switch it off
7 A are you doing/going to do B I might go

2 1 will have sold   6 will be travelling
2 will be recording   7 will have got over
3 will be lying   8 will have played
4 will have decided   9 will be bringing up
5 will be speaking   10 will have solved

3 1 waste 2 Take 3 In 4 on 5 had 6 from, to
7 takes 8 This

4 1 Genetic 2 scientists 3 biological 4 succeed
5 chemist 6 failure

5 a 1 keyboard 2 software 3 mouse 4 modem
5 document 6 website 7 printer 8 hardware

b 1 Scan 2 Attach 3 Press 4 Save 5 Enter
6 Search 7 Edit 8 Download 9 Insert

6 1 symptom 2 floppy 3 psychiatrist
4 terrify 5 umbrella

7 a B

b 1 B 2 C 3 C 4 B 5 A 6 B 7 A 8 A, B

8 Line 3: serius – serious
Line 4: to – too
Line 8: experienceing – experiencing
Line 10: scape – escape, dificult – difficult
Line 11: Marriing – Marrying
Line 12: recomended – recommended, Althought – Although
Line 16: there – their
Line 18: fell – feel

2 C

1 1 I took/I used to take   5 usually prescribes
2 had   6 watched/used to watch
3 was living, met   7 usually listen
4 had   8 felt/used to feel

2 a 1 having 2 print 3 working 4 talking 5 look up
6 be 7 talking 8 look like

b A 1 used to dress
2 used to be able to, is used to sleeping
3 get used to getting up
4 didn't use to look up

B 1 used to work
2 didn't use to have
3 get used to giving
4 used to be, is used to meeting

3 a -ility ability, possibility, responsibility
-ion addiction, concentration, corruption, expansion, obsession, restriction, tension
-ment argument, development, embarrassment, improvement, replacement

b 1 obsession   5 improvement
2 embarrassment   6 argument
3 addiction   7 possibility
4 restriction   8 ability

4 1 (✗) fed up **with**   2 (✓)   3 (✗) mad **about**
4 (✗) tired **of**   5 (✗) interested **in**   6 (✓)   7 (✗) keen **on**
8 (✗) addicted **to**   9 (✗) fascinated **by**   10 (✓)

5 1 get over   2 cut down   3 turned up   4 give up
5 getting on   6 sold out

6 a 2   **b** 1 F   2 F   3 T   4 T   5 F   6 T   7 F   8 F

7 1 Thanks/~~Thank you~~   2 ~~very nice~~/great
3 I'm really looking forward/~~I look forward~~
4 but/~~however~~   5 ~~would like~~/want
6 haven't got/~~don't have~~   7 ~~Are you able to~~/Can you
8 let me know/~~inform me~~   9 pick me up/~~collect me~~
10 One more thing/~~I have one more question~~

Listening

1 a Acupuncture is a very old Chinese technique which uses
needles to prevent or treat illness.

b 1 F   2 T   3 F   4 F   5 F   6 F   7 T   8 F

2 a 1 C   2 B   3 D   4 A

b a 1,4   b 4,3   c 2   d 3   e 1   f 2

Pronunciation

3 a 1 <u>a</u>llergy   2 app<u>oi</u>ntment   3 <u>fa</u>scinated   4 <u>vi</u>rus
5 bi<u>o</u>logist   6 <u>key</u>board   7 <u>tee</u>nager   8 la<u>bo</u>ratory
9 pre<u>scri</u>ption   10 <u>tran</u>quillizer   11 <u>swo</u>llen
12 a<u>ddic</u>ted   13 <u>in</u>teresting   14 <u>a</u>cupuncture
15 a<u>vai</u>lable

3 A

1 1 What **were** you searching for …?
2 Why **did you have** …?
3 While Julia **was looking** round …
4 Ten minutes after she **had taken** …
5 … when suddenly my computer **broke down**.
6 What **was the journalist writing** down …?
7 We **didn't have** enough time …
8 The plane **had** already landed …

2 1 had run out   2 Both are possible   3 had fallen down
4 Both are possible   5 had vanished

3 1 made   2 had been thinking   3 convinced   4 had
5 wrote   6 sent   7 was looking   8 saw   9 realized
10 had won   11 had forgotten   12 had written

4 a 1 ~~knowing~~/meeting   2 looked/~~seemed~~   3 ~~won~~/earned
4 ~~carrying~~/wearing   5 hoped/~~waited~~   6 ~~tell~~/say
7 ~~noticed~~/realized   8 knew/~~met~~   9 realized/~~noticed~~
10 ~~avoided~~/prevented   11 discussing/~~arguing~~
12 ~~remembered~~/reminded

b 1 b   2 a   3 a   4 b   5 a   6 b   7 b   8 a   9 b
10 a   11 a   12 b   13 b   14 a   15 b   16 a

5 /d/ argued, involved, mattered, prescribed, realized
/t/ influenced, pressed, published, searched
/ɪd/ avoided, edited, printed, tended, treated,

6 a 1 B   2 C   3 A

b 1 maid   2 judge   3 tormented   4 poodle   5 witness

c Story 1: the poodle
Story 2: Tommy's wife
Story 3: She left him because he didn't keep his promise.

7 1 Line 3: waked – woke   2 Line 4: was – were
3 Line 6: run – ran   4 Line 8: hurted – hurt
5 Line 8: was started – started   6 Line 9: haven't studied –
hadn't studied   7 Line 13: meet – met   8 Line 14: wasn't
wanting – didn't want   9 Line 15: learned – taught
10 Line 16: waited – hoped/expected

3 B

1 b 1 d   2 h   3 a   4 e   5 c   6 b   7 g   8 f

c 1 would have come   2 didn't have   3 would try
4 hadn't been   5 would have written down   6 weren't

2 1 shouldn't have chosen   5 shouldn't have drunk
2 should have gone   6 should have packed
3 should have set   7 should have taken
4 shouldn't have gone   8 should have been

3 a 2 dirty   3 scared/frightened   4 small   5 interested
6 cold   7 ugly   8 upset/sad   9 shocked   10 surprised

b 1 absolutely brilliant   4 absolutely starving
2 absolutely delighted   5 absolutely boiling
3 absolutely furious

4 1 cliff   2 rope   3 blizzard   4 drag   5 sledge/sleigh
6 struggle

5 /eɪ/ weight   /ɔɪ/ choice, boiling
/əʊ/ lower, rope   /ɪə/ nearer, really
/aɪ/ delighted, tiny   /eə/ scared, wear
/aʊ/ mountain, coward   /ʊə/ tour, furious

6 a He thought he would find the body near the Chinese
camp 6.

b 1 c   2 c   3 b   4 c

7 1 for   2 from   3 in   4 of   5 from
6 through   7 for   8 in

3 C

1 b 1 e   2 g   3 i   4 h   5 a   6 b   7 c   8 d   9 f

2 1 She must have had plastic surgery.
2 His illness can't have been very serious.
3 Their team must have won the match.
4 Someone might have dropped a cigarette or a match.
5 They can't have got lost.
6 He might be in the garden or (he might be) in the shower.

3 1 a   2 b   3 a   4 a   5 b   6 b   7 citizen
8 multi-ethnic   9 policy   10 run away

4 1 j   2 e   3 g   4 i   5 a   6 d   7 f   8 b   9 c   10 h

5 1 hand~~k~~erchief /'hæŋkətʃɪf/   2 dum~~b~~ /dʌm/
3 yog~~h~~urt /'jɒgət/   4 ~~k~~nig~~h~~t /naɪt/   5 recei~~p~~t /rɪ'siːt/
6 pa~~l~~m /paːm/   7 duve~~t~~ /'duːveɪ/   8 de~~b~~t /det/
9 fas~~t~~en /'faːsn/   10 ~~w~~hole /həʊl/

6 a 1 F   2 T   3 F   4 F   5 F   6 T   7 T   8 T

b 1 fleet *noun* a group of ships or boats that sail together
2 feeble *adj.* with no energy or power; weak
3 slipper *noun* a light soft shoe that is worn inside the
house
4 vain *adj.* too proud of your own appearance
5 portraits *pl noun* a picture, painting or photograph of a
person
6 blame *verb* to think or say that a certain person or thing
is responsible for sth bad that has happened

7 Suggested answers

1 He was born on 3rd April 1929 in Bristol, in south-west England.
2 During the Second World War his parents sent him away to stay with friends in the country.
3 He left school at the age of 16 and got a job as a civil servant.
4 He worked for 20 years and then retired in 1964.
5 He got married in 1953 and had three children.
6 Today he has eight grandchildren and he enjoys gardening and reading.

Listening

1 a Manolo and Jesús lost their jet skis and became trapped on a rock. They were eventually rescued by lifeguards.

b 1 on holiday – on business (line 2)
2 one morning – one afternoon (line 2)
3 they were both strong swimmers – although one of them was not a strong swimmer. (line 4)
4 although they were near the beach – they were far away (line 7)
5 piranhas – sharks (line 9)
6 for an hour – for half an hour (line 12)
7 lifeguards – the people at the jet-ski company (line 13)
8 his boss – his friend (line 15)

2 b They found the body of George Mallory. They identified it by a laundry label on it which said, 'G Mallory'.

c A 5 B 3 C 1 D 6 E 4 F 2

Pronunciation

3 1 exhausted 2 hideous 3 petrified 4 enormous
5 brilliant 6 amazed 7 horrified 8 delighted
9 monarchy 10 revolution 11 surrender 12 dictatorship
13 parliament 14 political 15 republic 16 government

4 A

1 b 1 ~~the red~~/the red one
2 ~~a skirt very old-fashioned~~/a very old-fashioned skirt
3 looser/~~more loose~~
4 ~~as well than~~/as well as
5 too tight/~~too tights~~
6 ~~more comfortable~~/most comfortable
7 ~~enough big~~/big enough
8 ~~the most pretty~~/the prettiest
9 as/~~than~~
10 too high/~~too much high~~
11 more boring/~~boringer~~
12 ~~food enough~~/enough food

2 1 (✓)
2 (✗) I heard some **beautiful classical** guitar music …
3 (✓)
4 (✗) I threw away those **hideous grey** trousers …
5 (✓)
6 (✗) We rented a **big old** country cottage …
7 (✗) … **blue suede** shoes for his birthday.
8 (✓)
9 (✗) She wore her **red silk** dress …
10 (✗) … **lovely purple cotton** jumper …?

3 1 The higher a mountain is, the riskier it is to climb.
2 The healthier your lifestyle (is), the longer you'll live.
3 The shorter the skirt (is), the slimmer you have to be to wear it.

4 The faster you speak, the more difficult it is to understand you.
5 The harder you work, the more I'll pay you.
6 The bigger a school is, the more impersonal it is.

4

E	J	T	R	I	H	S	T	A	E	W	S
D	R	E	S	S	I	N	G	G	O	W	N
J	E	V	S	M	E	O	R	A	W	O	S
L	A	D	N	A	S	T	I	E	A	L	Y
H	A	N	D	K	E	R	C	H	I	E	F
D	P	Y	J	A	M	A	S	P	S	B	S
T	S	E	V	T	R	I	K	S	T	N	E
B	L	O	U	S	E	N	D	R	C	A	V
N	S	L	I	P	P	E	R	S	O	S	O
B	T	R	I	H	S	R	A	P	A	C	L
C	T	R	A	C	K	S	U	I	T	R	G

5 1 get changed 2 hang your clothes up 3 fit 4 suit
5 dress up 6 match 7 try them on 8 get dressed

6 1 discount 2 catalogue 3 window-shopping
4 bargain 5 department store 6 casual
7 designer clothes 8 sales

7 a She had a problem with a pair of red velvet trousers she bought. They were too tight.

b A 4 B 6 C 1 D 5 E 3 F 2

8 Mick: 1 in 2 average 3 built 4 bald 5 moustache
6 beard 7 suit 8 T-shirt 9 trainers
Laura: 1 her 2 slim 3 shoulder 4 curly
5 skirt 6 belt 7 high-heeled

4 B

1 1 – 2 – 3 – 4 – 5 – 6 the 7 – 8 the 9 the
10 the 11 the 12 the 13 – 14 – 15 –

2 a 1 hadn't bought 2 would give 3 lived
4 hadn't argued 5 would do 6 hadn't told
7 didn't have to 8 had bought

b 1 hadn't got married 2 had travelled 3 went out
4 would turn off 5 had had 6 lived 7 would have
8 had bought 9 would knock it down

3 Across: 4 share 6 breadwinner 8 Ms 10 rate
11 sexism 12 feminist
Down: 1 Politically 2 partner 3 discrimination
5 masculine 7 roles 8 new

4 1 selfish 2 vain 3 jealous 4 mature 5 considerate
6 faithful 7 sensitive 8 organized

5 and 6 1 unimaginative 2 immature 3 unambitious
4 inefficient 5 disorganized 6 irresponsible
7 unsociable 8 untidy 9 illogical 10 impatient

7 a 1 men 2 women 3 men 4 women 5 women
6 men 7 men 8 women 9 men 10 men
11 women

b Reasons 3, 5 and 6.

8 Line 2: them Line 5: they Line 8: the
Line 3: of Line 6: much Line 9: the
Line 4: to Line 7: being Line 10: will

4 C

1 a **Always plural:** clothes, people, police
Uncountable: advice, furniture, luck, news, politics, toast, weather, work
Countable or uncountable: business, chocolate, glass, hair, iron, paper, wood

b 1 furniture, looks 2 jeans, suit 3 hair, needs
4 advice, helps 5 clothes, match 6 toast, got
7 money, means 8 people, are

2 1 had my blood pressure checked
2 is having his new computer delivered
3 do you have your hair cut
4 Have you had your eyes tested …?
5 am having my house redecorated
6 having your portrait painted

3 a 1 **oven:** the others are found in a bedroom
2 **porch:** the others are types of houses
3 **washing machine:** the others can be found in the kitchen
4 **path:** the others are all boundaries/form a barrier
5 **impersonal:** the others are all positive
6 **bookcase:** the others all provide heating
7 **turn on:** the others are all to do with putting things back in their right place
8 **fridge:** the others could all be found in a living room

b 1 ceiling 2 antique 3 chimney 4 pavement
5 gate 6 loo 7 path

c 1 change the bulb 2 turn the tap off.
3 lay the table 4 hang it up 5 lock the door

4 **-ous** dangerous, luxurious, religious
-able enjoyable, fashionable
-al historical, original, practical
-ful helpful, successful, useful

5 1 carry on 2 ran away 3 show him off 4 run out of
5 put out 6 put up with 7 put away 8 go with

6 a 1 inside 2 what/the things 3 sit

b 1 T 2 T 3 F 4 T 5 F 6 T 7 T 8 F

7 a Paragraph 1: Most young people … long summer holidays.
Paragraph 2: In the morning … not likely to go out.
Paragraph 3: The weekend begins … their homework!
Paragraph 4: The summer is … with their families.
Paragraph 5: In general, … did the same!

b **Suggested answers**
1 During the week/In the week/From Monday to Friday
2 At the weekend/Saturdays and Sundays
3 In the summer (holidays)

Listening

1 a 1 B 2 C 3 A 4 D

b a 2 b 4 c 3 e 1

2 a Yes, she thinks *feng shui* is out of control. She thinks there are too many people now claiming to be *feng shui* experts.

b 1 F 2 T 3 F 4 T 5 T

Pronunciation

2 1 skirt 2 shoes 3 short-sleeved 4 divorce 5 share
6 unsociable 7 sexist 8 impatient 9 cushion
10 stylish

5 A

1 b 1 It's the best book I **have ever** read.
2 I **have played/been playing** football since I was a little boy.
3 We **have been** together for six years.
4 I have known her **for** a long time.
5 You**'ve already told** me.
6 **Has he passed** his driving test yet?
7 Last month they **drove** to Morocco.
8 I **haven't seen** you for ages! How are you?

c 1 When did he arrive?
2 Have you finished yet?
3 How long have you lived here?
4 What time did you get up today?
5 Have you ever eaten octopus?
6 Did you see the film last night?
7 Have you seen Tom Hanks' new film?
8 What's the best novel you have ever read?

2 a 1 crashed 2 been running 3 had 4 bought
5 made 6 seen 7 seen 8 written 9 known
10 been waiting

b 1 haven't written 2 have been 3 have finished
4 have you been doing 5 have been going out
6 have decided 7 haven't told 8 Have you found
9 have been looking 10 haven't managed
11 haven't heard 12 has just arrived

3 1 butterfly 2 guinea pig 3 rabbit 4 fly 5 whale
6 octopus 7 shark 8 bear 9 bee 10 pigeon
11 cow 12 goat

4 1 puppy 2 snail 3 extinction 4 hunting 5 species
6 paws 7 kitten 8 feathers 9 sheep 10 wings
11 chicken 12 cages

5 1 e 2 b 3 d 4 c 5 a 6 f

6 a 1 He responds to human commands.
2 He writes autographs.

b 1 C 2 B 3 D 4 E 5 A

7 Para 1: F, H Para 3: G, J Para 5: E, K
Para 2: A, I Para 4: B, D

5 B

1 b 1 either 2 Both 3 both 4 neither 5 either

c 1 (✗) Does **anybody** know the right answer?
2 (✗) I don't know **anybody** who goes skiing.
3 (✓) 4 (✓) 5 (✓)
6 (✗) **No one/Nobody** knows if King Arthur really existed.
7 (✗) When you cook the dinner I can never find **anything** afterwards.
8 (✗) B No, **nothing**.

2 a 1 ~~none~~/no 2 All the/~~All~~ 3 Most/~~Most of~~
4 ~~All~~/Everything 5 ~~all days~~/every day
6 Anybody/~~Nobody~~ 7 all day/~~every day~~
8 ~~No~~/None

b Sentences 1, 3 and 6 can use *every* instead of *each*.

3 1 memorial 2 memory 3 souvenir 4 memory
5 reminder

4 1 addictive 2 harmless 3 obsession 4 losses
5 Unfortunately 6 seriously 7 socialize 8 probably

5 b 1 B 2 C 3 A

6 Line 1: writting – writing
Line 2: us – each other
Line 4: The last night – Last night
Line 5: remind – remember
Line 8: someone – anyone
Line 10: don't see – haven't seen
Line 11: married with – married to
Line 12: on June – in June
Line 13: write me – write to me
Line 14: to hear – to hearing

5 C

1 b 1 Mrs Brown, **who** has lived next door to me all my life, is a faith healer.
2 The presenter **whose** son is a mountaineer retired last year.
3 That's the laboratory **where** Tom works ~~there~~.
4 My mother gave me the chest of drawers **which/that** is in your bedroom.
5 The story (**which/that**) I read in the newspaper yesterday turned out not to be true.
6 Many animals **which/that** live in zoos are endangered species.
7 His operation, **which** lasted four hours, was completely successful.
8 My boss, **who is/who's** always pulling my leg, is a really funny person.

2 a 1 The man the puppies belong to …
2 The flat they moved into …
3 The organization my sister works for …
4 One of the women I work with …
5 His wife, who he had trusted completely, …

b 1 What 2 whom 3 which 4 which 5 what
6 which 7 whom 8 which 9 what

3 1 premonition 2 coincidence 3 ghost 4 soul
5 clairvoyant 6 telepathy 7 spooky

4 a 2 Meaning 1 3 Meaning 6 4 Meaning 5
5 Meaning 4 6 Meaning 2

b 1 glasses 2 draw 3 fair 4 fine 5 suit
6 point 7 calf

5 a 1 T 2 F 3 T 4 F 5 T 6 F 7 T

6 1 C 2 F 3 A 4 I 5 D 6 H 7 J 8 E 9 B 10 G

Listening

1 a She looked after a little boy who had fallen into her cage.

b 1 Chicago Zoo. 2 a 3 b 8 c 18 months
3 Five metres. 4 In the gorillas' cage.
5 She picked the boy up and carried him to the gate where the zookeepers were waiting.
6 To prepare her for the birth of her own baby.

2 a They're all about meeting someone.

b a 3 b 1 c 2 d 4

Pronunciation

2 1 en<u>vi</u>ronment 2 te<u>le</u>pathy 3 co<u>in</u>cidence 4 <u>spe</u>cies
5 volun<u>teer</u> 6 <u>mem</u>orize 7 chimpan<u>zee</u> 8 premo<u>ni</u>tion
9 <u>ill</u>egal 10 clair<u>voy</u>ant 11 re<u>sea</u>rch 12 <u>wild</u>life

3 a 1 science 2 pseudonym 3 lamb 4 foreign 5 knock
6 whistle 7 iron 8 calm 9 fascinated 10 answer

6 A

1 b 1 having 2 to escape 3 stop 4 going 5 live
6 to work out 7 not to tell 8 arrive 9 attacking
10 make

c 1 (✗) **Smoking** is prohibited here.
2 (✓)
3 (✗) I don't know where **to** get off the bus.
4 (✓) 5 (✓) 6 (✓)
7 (✗) It's not worth **going** to a clairvoyant.
8 (✗) The burglar got in without **making** a noise.
9 (✗) I'm looking forward to **seeing** you.
10 (✗) It took me ages to get used to **driving** on the left.

2 1 to find out 2 cleaning 3 to find 4 to empty
5 to rest 6 saving 7 inserting 8 seeing, to take

3 Across: 2 capital 5 fine 7 shoplifter 8 trial
13 evidence 14 arrest
Down: 1 magistrate 3 offence 4 verdict 6 pickpocket
9 witness 10 thief 11 steal 12 jury

4 1 commit 2 break 3 rob 4 steal 5 find 6 arrest
7 accuse 8 be tried 9 have 10 be released

5 1 daughter 2 suffer 3 coffee 4 throw 5 queue

6 a At major international events. Because he tried to rob the fastest man in the world.

b innocent 6 crowds 9 professional 8 catch 4 pickpocket 1
hand 3 police cell 2 expelled 10 arrested 5 lounge 7

7 Dear Sir/Madam,

I am writing to express my concern about the increase in street crime in my area, Central London.

On 22nd September last year, I was walking along Baker Street one evening when I was robbed by two young men wearing leather jackets and carrying knives. When I shouted, 'Help me!', the only person who was in the street, a man of about 40, did nothing and just walked away.

I would like to suggest to the public in general that if we do not help each other and stand up to criminals like these, none of us will be safe. As for the man who refused to help me, I would like to ask him one question: 'Would you like to be mugged and have your week's money stolen from you?'

Thank you for your attention.

Yours faithfully,

Mr R M Cole

6 B

1 b 1 Doreen asked Jim what time he had got home the night before.
2 Jim replied (that) he had arrived just before midnight.
3 Doreen asked where he had been from eight o'clock until midnight.
4 He replied (that) he had been working late.
5 Doreen said (that) he had worked late every night that week.
6 Jim told her (that) they had to finish the project by the end of the/that month.
7 Doreen asked him when they would have some time together.
8 Jim asked her to turn on the TV.
9 Doreen told him not to be so lazy.

2 a 1 My teacher advised me **to take** the exam.
2 James offered **to give** me a lift home.
3 He apologized for **breaking** the vase.
4 She asked me **not to tell** anybody.
5 The blackmailer **threatened to sell** the photos.
6 They agreed **to change** my jacket for a bigger size.

b 1 admitted killing him
2 reminded the jury not to be biased
3 denied stealing/having stolen the money
4 persuaded us to go on a safari together
5 recommended that I take/I took a taxi
6 regretted/regrets not studying more when she was younger

3 1 keep 2 truth 3 deceive 4 lies 5 cheat 6 white lie
7 pretend 8 catch

4 1 warned 2 threatened 3 encouraged 4 admitted
5 suggested 6 refused 7 apologized for 8 insisted on

5 b 1 truthful 2 secretive 3 not have a clue
4 pretentious 5 to cheat on (somebody)

6 /ð/ breathe, neither, rather, sunbathe, those, though
/θ/ breath, faithful, telepathy, thief, thought, threaten, truth, worth

7 a 1 B 2 D 3 A 4 C

b 1 The Library of Congress.
2 The FBI.
3 From the Pinkerton logo of a single staring eye and the words, 'The eye that never sleeps'.
4 They were not violent.
5 Forensic evidence suggests this is true.

8 2 agreed (to go) accepted 3 to remind me
4 promised (to go) 5 warned me 6 recommending
(that everyone watch) 7 apologized 8 insisted that I stay

6 C

1 a 1 Although/~~However~~ 2 ~~Though~~/On the other hand
3 However/~~Also~~ 4 also/~~as well~~
5 even though/~~on the other hand~~

b 1 so that 2 because of 3 so as not to 4 because
5 to 6 in spite of 7 Although 8 for 9 to

c 1 Tina told a white lie so as not to offend her friend.
2 Even though he'd been smoking for years, he didn't find it hard to give up. (He didn't … even though …)
3 Our flight was delayed because of the terrible storm.
4 Despite the awful jokes, everybody enjoyed his speech. (Everybody …)
5 I switched on the computer to check my e-mail.
6 He pretended to recognize her, although he couldn't remember who she was. (Although …)
7 I gave my daughter some money so that she could buy a Barbie doll.
8 In spite of the bad reviews, the film was a box-office success. (The film was …)

2 a 1 owe 2 inherit 3 give away 4 invest 5 waste
6 save

b 1 a safe 2 a credit card 3 a cash-point 4 a coin
5 a (bank)note 6 a cheque book

3 1 a 2 a 3 b 4 c 5 a 6 b 7 a 8 a

4 1 car 2 box 3 driving 4 name 5 business
6 control 7 bank 8 story

5 1 got away with 2 turned into 3 pick up
4 making up; grows up 5 caught out

6 a Barbie has a less 'feminine' image and a more 'realistic' shape.

b 1 D 2 C 3 B 4 A

c … they would vote for Barbie.

7 a 1 de<u>ve</u>loped 2 am<u>bass</u>ador 3 paedia<u>tri</u>cian
4 <u>a</u>verage 5 pro<u>por</u>tionate 6 <u>emph</u>asize 7 <u>correct</u>ness
8 <u>whee</u>lchair 9 dis<u>abi</u>lity 10 <u>eth</u>nic

8 Line 1: I been away – I have been away, in holiday – on holiday
Line 3: new work – new job
Line 3: much more better – much better
Line 5: Have you to sell – Do you have to sell
Line 8: adress – address
Line 11: wiht – with
Line 12: no news are better – no news is better
Line 13: keep on touch – keep in touch

LISTENING

1 a She was accused of shoplifting. She was not guilty.

b 1 F 2 T 3 T 4 F 5 T 6 F 7 F 8 F 9 T 10 F

2 a 1 E 2 C 3 B 4 D

b a 2, 4 b 3 c 1 d 3 e 4 f 1 h 2

PRONUNCIATION

2 a 1 <u>car</u> theft 2 <u>drug</u> dealing 3 a saf<u>a</u>ri park
4 a <u>dress</u>ing-gown 5 an <u>office</u> job 6 a <u>guinea</u> pig
7 a <u>life</u> sentence 8 a <u>track</u>suit 9 an <u>e</u>-mail
10 a <u>dish</u>washer 11 a <u>fire</u>place 12 a <u>health</u> centre

7 A

1 a 1 (✗) My cousin works **as** … 2 (✓)
3 (✗) Some people, **like** psychologists, …
4 (✗) My brother looks **like** my mother, …
5 (✗) …, so I missed the bus **as** usual. 6 (✓) 7 (✓)
8 (✗) He behaves **like** the boss, … 9 (✓) 10 (✓)

b 1 as 2 like 3 like 4 as 5 as 6 like 7 As 8 like

2 2 looks like 3 feel like 4 tastes 5 smells as if 6 feels
7 tastes like 8 look as if 9 sounds like 10 smell like

3

```
G  C  D  T  S  M  A  R  T  S  N  M
S  O  V  G  D  I  M  E  Z  O  C  Q
S  M  A  M  A  A  F  T  X  U  R  W
E  F  Z  V  M  S  T  T  C  R  U  E
L  O  A  P  P  E  T  I  Z  I  N  G
E  T  R  O  U  G  H  Y  B  C  J  C  R
T  H  T  A  S  T  Y  V  S  H  T
S  A  K  Y  H  E  S  A  L  T  Y
A  B  L  C  O  S  Y  P  U  O  R  Y  K
T  L  T  F  O  S  I  I  U  O  L  I
H  E  A  V  Y  F  C  R  D  N  I  I
G  S  P  O  O  K  Y  O  B  G  O  S
```

4 1 light blue 2 fair hair 3 sour almonds 4 dry wine
5 an easy exam 6 a soft bed 7 a mild curry
8 a cold bath 9 young people 10 new cars

5 a and **b**
1 It feels scratchy.   3 It smells fragrant.
2 It sounds deafening.   4 It tastes/smells fruity.

6 1 sun tan lotion 2 launch 3 efficiently
4 in the mood for 5 myth 6 in reverse 7 likely

7 1 for 2 to/with 3 on 4 to 5 in 6 as 7 on 8 of

8 1 She sounds as if she's got a cold.
2 Your old shoes are looking really scruffy.
3 The lights in my room are too dim.
4 You've bought a lot of apples.
5 Is there anything on at the cinema tonight?
6 Let's invite everyone we know to the party.

9 a The names of products or their slogans did not translate well into other languages.

b 1 Clairol 2 Coors 3 Parker 4 General Motors
5 Pepsi 6 Coca Cola

10 1 D 2 E 3 H 4 A 5 F 6 B 7 G 8 C

7 B

1 b 1 was set up 2 be made 3 exported 4 was made
5 was declared 6 has just been arrested
7 is being held 8 will be heard 9 will be released
10 be sent

2 1 It is said that crimes committed by young people are increasing.
2 It is thought that TV programmes and video games are to blame.
3 It is hoped that the government will take action.
4 It has been said that they are planning to ban all violent programmes.
5 It is not thought this will happen in the near future.

3 1 She is being taught French by her mother.
2 The workers were given some bad news (by the managing director).
3 The staff have been offered a pay increase (by the director).
4 I was promised the support of my colleagues/promised support from my colleagues/my colleagues' support.
5 My sister was sent the clothes she had ordered.

4 1 (✓) 2 (✗) owner 3 (✓) 4 (✗) client
5 (✗) colleague 6 (✓) 7 (✓) 8 (✓) 9 (✓)
10 (✗) customer

5 2 lift 3 tap 4 cupboard 5 rubbish 6 trousers
7 curtains

6 1 d 2 c 3 e 4 i 5 h 6 a 7 g 8 f 9 b

7 1 <u>in</u>crease 2 pro<u>test</u> 3 <u>per</u>mit 4 im<u>port</u>ed 5 in<u>sult</u>
6 <u>re</u>fund 7 pro<u>duce</u> 8 <u>pro</u>gress

8 a 1 Because cost is more important than quality.
2 Because Americans like things to be the same wherever they go.

b A 5 B 2 C 1 D 3 E 4

c 1 (✓) 2 (✗) 3 (✓) 4 (✗) 5 (✓) 6 (✗) 7 (✓)

9 a Against

b 1 Nowadays 2 where 3 advantages 4 main 5 as
6 which 7 who 8 Although 9 Compared
10 personally

7 C

1 a 1 so/~~such~~ 2 ~~so~~/such 3 so/~~such~~ 4 so/~~such~~ 5 ~~so~~/such
6 so/~~such~~ 7 so/~~such~~ 8 ~~so~~/such 9 ~~so~~/such

b 1 His trousers were so tight that he couldn't sit down.
2 It was such a bad joke that nobody laughed.
3 They were such inexperienced climbers that they needed rescuing.
4 There were so many/such a lot of different brands that I didn't know which to choose.
5 My niece is so shy/such a shy girl that everyone makes fun of her.
6 My neighbours made such a terrible noise that I couldn't get to sleep.

2 1 have 2 to 3 who/that 4 the 5 should/ought to
6 been 7 for 8 as 9 to 10 up 11 each
12 everyone/everybody 13 no 14 what 15 would

3 **-dom** freedom
-ity maturity, responsibility
-ness weakness, happiness
-tion appreciation, ambition
-th length, strength
-t guilt, complaint
-hood neighbourhood, childhood
-ship leadership, relationship

4 **Across:** 2 pick up 4 forward 7 rug 10 write 11 tail
12 run 14 eventually 17 tap 18 set up 19 tight
22 roof 24 encourage

Down: 1 defeat 2 plain 3 prescription 5 debt
6 sexist 8 untidy 9 trial 13 neighbourhood 15 ant
16 laptop 20 goat 21 get 23 flu

5 1 especially 2 scientific 3 dictatorship 4 fashionable
5 luxurious 6 extinction

6 a Anne Hathaway

b 1 F 2 T 3 T 4 F 5 F 6 F 7 F 8 T 9 T 10 F

LISTENING

1 b You can find Starbucks coffee shops everywhere.

c 1 c 2 a 3 b 4 c

2 a *A Midsummer Night's Dream* 4   *The Merchant of Venice* 1
Romeo and Juliet 2   *The Tempest* 3

b a 4 b 2 c 1 e 3

PRONUNCIATION

1 a 1 I wouldn't like to run an international company.
2 Our competitors are launching a new product in April.
3 There's a chain of restaurants with three branches in the centre.
4 He made an enormous profit in only two and a half years.
5 The owner of our school lives abroad.

2 a 1 The <u>lead</u> singer lives in <u>Leeds</u>.
2 Her <u>fa</u>ther had a <u>heart</u> trans<u>plant</u>.
3 What's the dog got in its <u>paw</u>? Is it a <u>thorn</u>?
4 Her comp<u>u</u>ter stopped w<u>or</u>king on the <u>first</u> of <u>March</u>.
5 Look! You've dropped <u>food</u> on your new s<u>ui</u>t!

3 a 1 **The** supermarket chain **was** founded **in the** States.
2 A colleague **of** mine **has been** arrested **for** theft.
3 **The** staff **were** told **to** work overtime.
4 **We've** found **a** factory **that can** make **the** product.
5 **Our** company's going **to be** taken over **by a** multinational